WASTE AGE
WHAT CAN DESIGN DO?

the
**DESIGN
MUSEUM**

CONTENTS

DIRECTOR'S FOREWORD
Tim Marlow

The term 'Waste Age' is a provocation. In the spirit of past material ages from Stone to Steam, it highlights the fact that one of the most pervasive materials of our time is, in fact, waste. It's a condition that needs to be stated to be understood and ultimately to be changed. But waste is not just a damaging by-product, it's also a resource, and one that we need to learn to value and utilise. Furthermore, the implications of addressing our enormous flows of waste are vast and critical – for design, for the economy, for society and of course for the environment.

In both this book and the major exhibition it accompanies, we ask: What can design do? Let's consider that question for a moment. The construction industry accounts for 38 per cent of all carbon emissions. The fashion industry is often cited as the world's second largest polluter, after aviation, creating 92 million tonnes of textile waste a year. Meanwhile, by far the greatest source of plastic pollution is packaging. Designers and architects are obviously heavily implicated in these problems, but design is also part of the solution, crucial to creating the changes we need. The question is: how much agency do *designers* have to challenge the systems they serve?

What we present in this book is a selection from a groundswell of innovative thinking about how to reduce and reverse our addiction to waste. There is a focus on reuse, on recycling, on new materials, on the organic, on different social approaches – and sometimes on a return to ancient principles. The book presents no simple answers but acknowledges that every product is part of a complex system and always exists at a particular point in a lifecycle. Getting to grips with that complexity – and not just seeing a product as an end in itself – is part of the difficult work we need to undertake.

It is clear that we have very little time to address the climate crisis. The Design Museum aims to contribute to the sense of urgency – but also to the sense of opportunity – by focusing our attention on that area where design has the greatest potential impact – on waste.

I would like to thank Dassault Systèmes, Cockayne Grants for the Arts and The London Community Foundation for their generous support in helping us stage the exhibition. We have sought a broad spectrum of advice in realising this project and I would like to thank all who have contributed, in particular our advisory committee (listed on page 271) for the range and depth of their knowledge and their intellectual agility in confronting an issue that is fundamental to the future of the planet.

The frame of a television cast in copper reclaimed from
e-waste at the Agbogbloshie dump, Ghana, by Ibrahim Mahama
(see page 62).

INTRODUCTION
Justin McGuirk

The traditional opposition between 'nature' and 'culture' is problematic for any number of reasons, but there is one reason that is rarely discussed. The 'nature vs culture' dualism leaves out an entire domain that properly belongs to neither: the world of waste. The mountains of waste that we produce every year, the torrents of polluting effluent, the millions of tonnes of greenhouse gases, the new cosmos of microplastics expanding through our oceans – none of this has ever been entered into the ledger under 'culture'. Of all the products of human hands, it is the oeuvre that no one wants to own, discuss or preferably even see. At the same time, it is no longer assimilable into 'nature' in the way that the waste of human civilisations was for millennia before the Industrial Revolution. This new, 'improved' waste is incompatible with the Earth – too chemical, too durable, too noxious and, ultimately, too voluminous.

This would suggest that waste is a third category, distinct from the others – but that is not quite right either. In fact, waste is precisely what obliterates the distinction between nature and culture. At this point, when the very weather is warped by climate change and plankton thousands of metres deep have intestinal tracts full of microplastics, the idea of a nature that is pristine or untouched is delusional. Nature and waste have fused at both planetary and microbiological scales. Similarly, one should argue that waste is not merely culture's by-product but that it *is* culture – and that we have produced a *culture of waste*. In this case, to focus our gaze on waste is not an act of morbid negativity; it is an act of cultural realism in the spirit of earlier realists, from Karl Marx and Gustave Courbet to Pier Paolo Pasolini. For if waste is the mesh that entangles nature and culture, then it may be the defining material of our age. Representing it and understanding it are the first steps towards change.

If one looks at the material ages of popular history, from the Stone Age and the Bronze Age onwards, there is an illusory sense of hard things dematerialising. The Steam Age and the Information Age conjure up ineffable clouds of moisture and data. In fact, the opposite is true. The Steam Age, for instance, launched the great explosion of material goods that has only mushroomed exponentially ever since. The statistics that accompany our current rates of waste are mind-numbing. What does it mean to say, as one recent report does, that by 2050 as much as 12 billion tonnes of plastic will have accumulated in landfills or the natural environment? What does it mean to say that more than a million plastic bags are consumed every minute globally, and that this amounts to between 500 billion and 1.5 trillion a year? Such numbers present a seemingly precise quantification that is at the same time utterly ungraspable. The average person just translates them into 'a lot' or 'a shitload'.

This is where the naming of ages becomes useful. The Anthropocene, or the age of human-driven planetary change, has the benefit of evoking the new geological layer that we are forming through our waste deposits. What more literal entanglement of nature and waste can we imagine than a new planetary crust composed of our fossil-fuel residues? But some prefer a more political definition, the Capitalocene, which fingers a specific economic system – capitalism – that has been dominant for 500 years, a mere blip in the history of humanity. To say that we live in a Waste Age is to acknowledge both the geological and the economic positions. It is to acknowledge that culture produces not just architecture and infrastructure and digital technology but also a million plastic bags a minute and 60 million Apple AirPods a year (with a usable lifespan of a few years each but an actual lifespan of, who knows, millennia?). It is to acknowledge that growth, the engine of capitalism, is entirely dependent on the reliable and ruthlessly efficient generation of waste.

Readers may feel that this is an ungenerous and rather pessimistic categorisation of human activity in the twenty-first century. On the contrary: invoking the Waste Age offers the opportunity for a radical shift in late-capitalist civilisation. Only by acknowledging the scale of the waste crisis can we reorient society and the economy towards less polluting modes of producing, consuming and living. The problem is that waste has always been a marginal issue, both literally and figuratively – it has been dumped in and on the peripheries. It has always been treated as an 'externality', an unavoidable by-product of necessary industrialisation. But it is now an internality – internal to every ecosystem and every digestive system from plankton to humans. If waste truly were to be a central issue – brought into the heart of every conversation about how things are extracted, designed and disposed of – it would transform society and present a structural challenge to our current globalised economics. To invoke the Waste Age is to usher in the transition to a cleaner future.

We have to remind ourselves that waste as a phenomenon at any scale is a relatively recent concept. It was only with the advent of the Industrial Revolution, and its massive stimulation of production, that the material by-products of extraction and manufacturing began to accumulate in mountainous heaps. In that sense, as much as Britain likes to claim the Industrial Revolution, it must also own the invention of waste.[1] The modern concept, then, is only 250 years old. On the other hand, it is striking how long ago the symptoms were diagnosed. Not only was William Morris already railing against the 'waste' of machine-made products in the late nineteenth century but, decades later, critics of post-war America also pinpointed all the forces that have led us to our environmental crisis. And in the ensuing seventy-plus years, nothing has changed except the sheer scale of planetary degradation.

In 1960, Vance Packard published *The Waste Makers*, a searing critique of 1950s America in its full consumerist pomp. He details at length the different forms of planned obsolescence, from products designed to fail to those designed to be simply more desirable than last year's model. And at almost every level of society, it is understood that such obsolescence is a necessary feature of a healthy economy – from politicians to cynical businessmen to disillusioned (but compliant) designers to consumers who think it is their patriotic duty to support the economy. The very idea of the 'lifetime guarantee' conjured up the spectre of unemployment and shuttered factories. *The Waste Makers* is an X-ray of the American way of life – a society that replaced scarcity with overabundance, force-fed on easy credit and urban sprawl. And yet what is most striking about the book is that at no point does Packard envision an ecological catastrophe. Instead, he sees the problem as largely ethical. Yes, he worries about the depletion of natural resources (a purely extractivist logic, and a problem that was largely solved by globalisation), but in the main his concern is *moral decay*. He bemoans the 'sell, sell, sell' commercialisation of everyday life and the entrenchment of hedonistic consumerism.

The Waste Makers is also an object lesson in how the modernist project was perverted. The ideal of well-designed, mass-produced goods that were affordable to all and that could offer even the poorest a better quality of life was a dependable vision of social progress for the first half of the twentieth century. What Packard demonstrates is how that ideal was warped by the financial imperatives of business and the broader economy – in other words, how waste was absolutely integral to an even higher ideal: growth. Perhaps modernism's faith in the principle of universally available industrial goods – at least when applied on a planetary scale – was always incompatible with the planet. But it does seem extraordinary from our vantage point to think that even in 1960 the environmental impact of waste was not worth a mention. Two years later, Rachel Carson's *Silent Spring*, about the devastating effects of agricultural pesticides, would start to wake people up to the problem.

Contrary to what we might assume, wastefulness is not a natural human instinct – we had to be taught how to do it. Disposability was one of the great social innovations of the post-war years. When the first disposable products became available in the 1950s, from TV-dinner meal trays to plastic bags, consumers had to be persuaded that this magical new substance – plastic – was not too good to be thrown away. They had to be instructed in the advantages of the throwaway society. Corporations – in particular, the petrochemicals industry – spent years and millions of dollars lobbying for the replacement of paper grocery bags with plastic ones. With the advent of supermarkets, and a help-yourself service culture, every product now had to be individually packaged to survive on the shelves. And with the full bloom of convenience culture and takeaway everything, disposability reached its apogee.

In 1950, the world produced about 2 million tonnes of plastic each year. Today, it is 368 million tonnes,[2] with more plastic produced in the last decade than ever before. Nearly half of all plastic waste (forty-seven per cent) comes from packaging, while fourteen per cent comes from textiles. As David Farrier writes in his book *Footprints: In Search of Future Fossils*, 'it is likely that every single piece of plastic ever produced and not incinerated still exists somewhere in some form'.[3] There are believed to be more than 5 trillion pieces of plastic in the world's oceans. Many of these are in the gyre known as the Great Pacific Garbage Patch. In his novel *The Peripheral*, William Gibson accelerates this diffuse mess into an eighth continent: a plastic landmass inhabited by transhuman 'Patchers'. It's a darkly humorous piece of dystopian fiction, and one that anticipated the fact that the plastics industry is in no mood to shrink – in fact, fossil-fuel companies, bracing themselves for a drop in petrol use, are gearing up to massively increase plastics production. And who will stop them?

To say that we live in the Waste Age is not to focus attention on an unpleasant but marginal problem; it is to say that the production of waste is absolutely central to our way of life – that waste is deliberately generated as the very metabolism of our economics. And while the waste crisis and the climate crisis are not the same thing, waste is a major driver of climate change. The plastics indus- try is the second-largest producer of industrial greenhouse gases[4], and methane generated in landfills is another significant contributor. But to invoke the Waste Age is also to claim that waste is one of the great material resources of our time. It acknowledges the tremen- dous untapped value in what we throw away. Take the tens of millions of tonnes of electronic waste that we discard every year. Instead of recycling it, countries like the UK have been shipping it to Ghana – where it amasses in the vast Agbogbloshie e-waste dump. At the time of writing, the Ghanaian government has started to shut down the dump because it is so toxic, but for years it has been picked over by an informal local economy mining it for precious metals and valua- ble parts. The methods may have been noxious – plastic wires were burned to release the copper – but the principle is sound. Some esti- mate that by 2080 the largest metal reserves will not be underground but in circulation as existing products. About seven per cent of the world's gold supplies, for instance, are trapped inside electronics. Suddenly the notion of 'above-ground mining' starts to make sense.[5]

You may think that what I am about to suggest is that recycling is the answer to this crisis. Far from it. Recycling rates are pathetically inadequate and, in a country like the UK at least, the system is essentially broken. Indeed, the very notion of recycling only validates the production of more virgin plastics and other materials – as if it's alright because they will be recycled, when they won't. Recycling will play an important role in the transition to the new economy – what- ever that looks like – but it is not enough on its own. And it should be stressed that any attempts to blame consumers for the waste crisis or the failures of recycling are, at best, wide of the mark and, at worst, deeply cynical. This was patently illustrated recently when it emerged that more than half of the plastic that the British government said had been recycled had instead been shipped abroad to be incin- erated – in 2020, more than 200,000 tonnes of our 'recycled' plastic was dumped and burned in Turkey.[6] What a mockery of the consumer labour that went into sorting and rinsing yoghurt pots and milk bottles.

Similarly, it should also be stressed that post-consumer waste is only a small part of the problem. When it comes to e-waste, for example, by far the greatest percentage of waste has already been produced before a device is even purchased – the mining and manufacturing processes generate quantities of waste that no amount of recycling after the fact can even come close to remediating. Since most of this waste happens 'upstream', before shoppers put their hands in their pockets, the onus is on governments to legislate just as they have on any number of issues in the past – from the banning of chlorofluorocarbons in fridges to the adoption of tempered glass in car windscreens. Manufacturers, too, must shoulder their responsibilities, but cannot be relied upon. And so, finally, we come to the role that designers can and will play.

It goes without saying that design has been one of the driving forces behind our prodigious waste streams in the last century. As the handmaidens of commerce, designers have been utterly complicit in the throwaway economy, from planned obsolescence to the promotion of convenience culture to entombing products in layers of seductive packaging to what designers do best: creating desire. Paradoxically, even when designers achieve a sense of permanence it is illusory – the iPhone, from about the fourth generation onwards, achieved the platonic ideal of the smartphone only to be replaced year after year because of software innovations and the need to stimulate new sales. However, the culture of design is changing: one has only to look at an emerging generation of designers that has very little interest in producing more stuff and is much more invested in understanding the extractive processes behind products and the afterlives that they progress on to.

The outlook of young designers today is very different from that of their predecessors. Shorn of blissful ignorance and only too alert to the mounting crisis around us, many have reinvented themselves as material researchers, waste-stream investigators and students of global economic flows. The object is no longer an end in itself but a vehicle towards understanding the complex systems that produce it and the even more opaque systems that dispose of it. This kind of systems thinking is absolutely essential for reducing waste and pollution at every stage of an object's life, from extraction to decomposition. If every product was evaluated in terms of how much waste it generated or how brief its lifespan was likely to be, it would transform the discipline and consumer behaviour. And in many cases those objects would not be brought into being. It's like that Cedric Price anecdote about the bickering couple who wanted him to design their house – they didn't need a house, they needed a divorce. What, you may ask, should designers do in practical terms to address this crisis. Many of the principles of good design for the twenty-first century are well understood and already being implemented in certain quarters. For a start, objects can be designed to be readily repairable, which means not using proprietary screws and glues or other strategies for preventing repair. Electronics can be designed with modular parts – like the Fairphone and the Framework laptop – so that batteries, memories and motherboards can be replaced as they decline or evolve. Products should be designed for easy disassembly and recycling, which means not fusing different plastics or metals together so that they cannot be recycled. When it comes to construction and the built environment, which is the biggest carbon emitter of all, we need a major shift towards adapting and reusing perfectly good buildings rather than demolishing and replacing them for marginal financial gains. We should be reducing our reliance on carbon-heavy steel and concrete, and turning to naturally grown materials such as sustainably managed cross-laminated timber.

What agency do designers even have to implement such strategies when their immediate responsibility is to fulfil the briefs set by their paymasters? After all, the last thing any politician or manufacturer wants to see is reduced production. Well, designers need to become consummate persuaders. And as the general public becomes more aware and more demanding, manufacturers will feel more pressure to change – and more fundamentally than the current epidemic of 'greenwashing' suggests. But what seems clear is that if the principles outlined above were widespread, it would challenge the industrial paradigm of the last 100 years. What does a society look like in which fridges last fifty years, not five, and where individual ownership of certain goods is replaced by communal sharing? What does a world of distributed manufacturing look like, in which distant factories and global shipping give way to more local or bioregional, artisanal production? What are the implications of a world in which some products last forever and others, made of organic materials, will decompose in days?[7] Our aesthetic sensibilities may have to adapt. After nearly a century of appreciating the hard-smooth-shiny perfection of plastics, we may begin to embrace irregularity, imperfection, decay and decomposition.

There is hope, of sorts, in mushrooms. It is true that mycelium has become the experimental material du jour, used in everything from bricks to handbags, but that is not the hope that I was referring to. Rather, it is the fungus as a metaphor – an organism that can not only survive but even thrive in damaged landscapes, and help to restore them. Anna Lowenhaupt Tsing has written compellingly about the ability of the matsutake mushroom to revive pine forests that have been ravaged by fire. 'Matsutake's willingness to emerge in blasted landscapes', she writes, 'allows us to explore the ruin that has become our collective home'.[8] Mycorrhizal fungi create symbiotic networks with tree roots, nourishing them and enabling life after ecological catastrophe. This is a powerful demonstration of what Tsing calls 'entangled ways of life', and it is precisely that entanglement that designers are beginning to learn – the way in which every object is connected to the world, through myriad social and ecological processes, from raw material to waste material. And just as the twentieth century was a summer of plenty, when we could consume and discard with abandon, so the twenty-first century will be defined by an autumnal scarcity, in which we have to be more resourceful and sparing – keeping our eyes trained on the forest floor.

01 PEAK WASTE

E-WASTE AS A CHALLENGE
FOR DESIGN AND SOCIETY
Josh Lepawsky

1   Opposite:
An e-waste recycling
facility, managed by
Recupel, Belgium

By the 2030s–40s, if current rates continue, consumers will discard in excess of 100 million tonnes of electronic devices globally per year. More than just sheer mass, these discarded electronics, often known as 'e-waste', are also allegories. Stories about them narrate dreams of shiny technological futures and nightmares of social and ecological break-down. These stories are important for the ways in which they have drawn attention to electronics as a source of toxic harm, but they also mistake a part for a whole. Post-consumer disposal of electronics constitutes just one node in the networks of resource extraction, manufacturing and consumption that comprise the lives of electronics, and is not the great-est source of pollution or waste. Moreover, the incessant focus on what happens to devices after consumers dispose of them makes it ever more difficult to draw attention 'upstream' to the mining and manufacturing processes that bring electronics into being, and in which the most signif-icant pollution and waste effects arise. Neither repair nor recycling is sufficient to mitigate the magnitude of challenges posed by pollution and waste arising from electronics. Such necessary but insufficient meas-ures will have to be combined with radically different design practices and reworked business models for real, substantive change to occur.

WHAT'S THE PROBLEM WITH E-WASTE?
A hundred million tonnes of e-waste piling up some time in the not-too-distant future might sound like a big problem, but the chal-lenges that such a number suggests are both already here and more complex than those posed by mere tonnage alone. Today, a single copper mine operating for 336 days (i.e. less than a year) generates as much waste by weight as those 100 million tonnes of post-consumer e-waste projected to arise in the 2030s–40s. The electronics sector is the second-largest consumer of copper globally (the first is elec-trical wiring for buildings – wiring that, of course, digital devices rely on for electricity). Every kilogram of copper mined and made availa-ble for use entails more than 210 kilograms of mine waste. The waste rock from copper mining involves the release of toxic heavy metals. Water that percolates through this waste can generate acidic leachates that harm the people, places and things through which they pass.
        After mining, the largest mass of waste comes from making electronics. In the European Union (EU), the manufacturing of electronics produces 18.7 million tonnes of waste per year. This figure may seem

large, but notice that it is an order of magnitude smaller than what arises from that single copper mine. Meanwhile, discarded electronics collected from EU households – this is the stuff usually called e-waste or waste electrical and electronic equipment (WEEE) – comes to 3.8 million tonnes, two orders of magnitude below that one copper mine and an order of magnitude less than electronics manufacturing in the EU.

Yet a singular focus on mass has important limits for understanding the challenge presented by pollution and waste arising from electronics. A kilogram of copper, a kilogram of trichloroethylene (TCE, used as a solvent in manufacturing electronics) and a kilogram of sulphur hexafluoride (SF_6, used in etching processes) are all the same mass, but their toxicological profiles and contributions to global heating are radically different from each other.

TCE has been found to be 'carcinogenic in humans by all routes of exposure' and induces toxic harm in the central nervous system, immune system and other organs.[1] It is one among many chemicals used to manufacture electronics and their components. While they are used in manufacturing processes, these chemicals are not intended to end up in those components or devices – nor are they intended to enter people's bodies or environments. Yet they do and, at the same time, are rarely if ever included in the definition of e-waste despite meeting at least some definitions of waste more generally. In the EU, for example, a legal definition of waste includes a 'residual substance derived from a production or consumption cycle in a manufacturing or combustion process'.[2]

Legacy releases of TCE and other chemicals haunt Silicon Valley today. These chemicals leak from underground storage tanks and seep into groundwater in parts of the Valley. One such place that has received significant study is called the Middlefield-Ellis-Whisman (MEW) Area. MEW is just one of several Superfund clean-up sites in Silicon Valley related to the legacy of electronics manufacturing ('Superfund' is a shorthand term used to refer to a legislative framework in the United States governing the use of tax dollars for the clean-up of industrial sites). Today, it is where some of Google's and other Big Tech's facilities are sited. An engineering study examining the prospects for clean-up of the MEW found that it would require US$1 billion and a minimum of 500 years to reach current standards for safe drinking water.[3] Such wildly disjunctive figures – $1 billion dollars amortised over five centuries – hint at the broader challenges posed by pollution and waste arising from electronics. Those challenges take on the qualities of waste-management problems often associated with 'exotic' stuff like nuclear waste, and yet most of the devices from which these problems arise are handled by many people every day, myself included.

Of course, one of the most pressing concerns is the way in which devices like phones, laptops, desktops, tablets and the networks that they run on contribute to climate breakdown. Apple's environmental-sustainability reports are particularly illuminating here. The company is sure to emphasise its progress towards sustainability – but its own data in these reports show, for example, that over eighty per cent of the carbon footprint of the latest iPhone comes from manufacturing it while only fourteen per cent arises from its use.[4] No amount of recycling by users of those phones can recoup the amount of carbon emitted during their manufacture.

When it comes to the global heating attributable to electronics, consider the example of sulphur hexafluoride (SF_6) already mentioned above. The trouble with SF_6 has less to do with toxicity and more with its global-warming potential: it is part of a suite of greenhouse gases used to manufacture electronics devices such as screens for monitors used in phones, computers and televisions. Currently, there are no replacements for these gases used in electronics manufacturing, yet they are hundreds or thousands of times more potent greenhouse gases than carbon dioxide. Electronics manufacturers are actively developing carbon mitigation and removal strategies. However, the strategies that already exist – from rehabilitation of savannah and mangrove forests to wind and solar farms for renewable energy – all presume ready access to Indigenous land.[5] Yet it is an open question whether people whose lands these are will accept such projects.

The issue of carbon mitigation and removal, briefly sketched here, highlights some of the broader complexity that pollution and waste from electronics bring with them beyond sheer mass. That complexity could be called 'incommensurability' – that is, an inability to be judged by the same standards. There is no common register on which to reconcile specific forms of mass, toxicity and global-warming potential, let alone how these intersect with ongoing forms of colonialism (e.g. presuming access to Indigenous lands for remediation and mitigation projects). Reducing one problem does not necessarily lead to reductions in the others. Thus, designers, in making technical choices, are implicitly, if not explicitly, engaged in bringing ethical relations – questions about good and right action – literally into being in the electronic products that their designs result in.

CIRCULAR ECONOMIES?

Post-consumer repair and recycling are necessary, but they are not sufficient to overcome the challenges of waste and pollution from electronics. Both repair and recycling share the shortcoming of dealing with waste after it already exists. By the time devices are ready for repair or recycling, their fates have already been sealed by chemical toxicity, durability and repairability among other characteristics decided upstream by designers and manufacturers. These fates define the range of possibilities for dealing with devices in repair or recycling.

Post-consumer recycling cannot match the tonnage, toxicity, heterogeneity or harms of pollution and waste arising in the mining for, or manufacture of, digital devices. However, this situation does *not* mean that post-consumer recycling should be abandoned. It is also important to remember that recycling in upstream phases of mining and manufacturing is very different, in terms of logistics and conservation value, than in 'downstream' post-consumer recycling.

Even as recycling takes on a new name in attempts at creating 'circular economies', its limits must be recognised. A genuinely circular economy is impossible to achieve if it is still premised on growth. Why? Once amalgamated into parts and components, materials used in electronics are often too complex to recycle back into pure enough fractions without the addition of new rounds of energy and material inputs. Those new rounds of energy and materials have to come from somewhere; the shift to renewables cannot fully overcome this problem (you have to build the renewable infrastructure out of something, for example). In some cases, it remains technically impossible to separate some amalgams of materials.[6] Also, a 'circular' but growing economy means that energy and materials are being added to it. Again, those materials and energy have to come from somewhere.[7] While post-consumer repair and recycling are both important, they are also mismatched to the challenges of pollution and waste arising from electronics for which they are all too often assumed to be a solution.

DESIGN (AND ITS LIMITS)

Designers have the power to increase the service life of devices. Prolonging service life is an important form of material and energy conservation since the longer a device is used, the longer the period of time over which the material and energy that it embodies is amortised. There are many design paths along which to achieve such goals. They include:

1   Design for repair. Design decisions should be avoided that make it difficult or impossible for consumers or repair technicians to affordably fix devices. One such class of choices that is increasingly common across many categories of device (e.g. laptops, monitors, phones, tablets and even some desktops) is their design as sealed, one-piece ('fused') units, often using adhesives rather than screws or similar fasteners. This type of design is sometimes called a 'slate' form factor in the industry (form factor refers to the appliance's size, shape and style, and 'slate' to its reliance on a touchscreen rather than physical buttons). It brings with it the loss of device characteristics that used to be quite common, such as user-detachable and replaceable batteries.[8]

2   Reduce the types of materials. Material diversity often complicates the recycling of end-of-life devices by making increasingly likely the cross-contamination of material fractions (e.g. non-ferrous scrap mingled in with plastic fragments).

3   Increasing modularity. Greater modularity can increase the likelihood of device reuse by enabling upgrades or replacement of parts, rather than having to retire whole devices (e.g. soldering RAM to a motherboard reduces modularity whereas slotting RAM onto the board enables replacement/upgrade). Longer use conserves energy and the materials embodied in devices.

4   Avoiding serialisation – i.e. using hardware or software identifiers to match parts. Serialisation can increase the barriers to repair by users and/or third-party and independent repair operations.[9] Making repair more difficult risks reducing material and energy conservation by shortening the useful lives of devices and, thus, negatively impacting on sustainability outcomes.

5   Examining which combinations of materials and assemblies enhance durability, repairability and remanufacturing options. The greater the durability and the more options that exist for repair

and/or remanufacturing, the greater the potential for conserving the energy and materials embodied in devices.

6   Using recycled (or scrap) materials. This generally offers substantial energy and material savings over the use of primary raw materials, the mining of which is the largest source of pollution and waste arising from the lives of electronics.

7   Pursuing clean(er) and green(er) product chemistry. Clean(er), green(er) chemistry reduces the risks of toxic harm to the people manufacturing the devices, to those involved in waste management and to environments.

More broadly, designers might mitigate the pollution and waste consequences of electronics by orienting their practices away from questions about risk (e.g. 'How much TCE can we use before workers get poisoned?') and towards questions about alternatives (e.g. 'Which safe(r) chemical could be used instead of TCE?'); or instead of asking, 'How can the per unit energy or material efficiency of Product X be reduced by Y per cent?' ask instead, 'How could the aggregate throughput of energy and materials for Brand X's products be reduced?' Risk analyses generally operate to bolster the status quo. Thinking instead about alternatives is oriented towards finding different ways of doing things (which is another way of saying that alternatives are about 'innovation').[10]

The power of product design also has its limits. Pollution and waste arise from industrial systems; product designers formulate specific models of, for example, phones, computers and tablets. Between industrial system and industrially produced device lies a mismatch of scale. Designing clean(er), green(er), more efficient and repairable appliances while manufacturing ever larger numbers of them in an industrial system premised on growth is unlikely to overcome the challenges of pollution and waste arising from electronics.

Ecological economists have a name for this enigma: they call it the 'rebound effect' or, sometimes, the 'Jevons Paradox'. William Stanley Jevons was a nineteenth-century political economist who studied the use of coal in industrialising England. He found something seemingly odd going on: as machines became more efficient at using coal, the use of coal increased. What Jevons would come to realise is that per-unit efficiency does not necessarily lead to aggregate efficiency. He came to understand that this contradiction arose because improved per-unit efficiency made it cheaper to use a given material – in this case, coal. As the cost of using the fuel declined, more people using more machines could use greater quantities of coal than they could before the efficiency gains were realised. Thus, aggregate demand for coal rose. The Jevons Paradox remains relevant to the contemporary electronics industry. If a designer finds a way to cut the use of, say, SF_6 by ten per cent per screen built, but the number of screens manufactured grows by ten per cent, then the per-unit efficiency gain is wiped out in aggregate.

If designers want to contribute to real reductions of pollution and waste from electronics, they must turn their attention upstream – to the ways in which industrial systems make electronics in the first place, long before consumers have, for example, their phones in their hands.

THIS IS NOT YOUR GOLDMINE.
THIS IS OUR MESS.
Liz Ricketts

Dear Fashion Industry,
Let's talk about waste.

We are on the verge of a waste revolution – a revolution of waste technology and of systems driven by a revolution in the way we think about waste. Some people and organisations call this revolution the Circular Economy. Others prefer the language of regenerative systems. Whatever model or lexicon we choose, waste is quickly moving from out of sight, out of mind to the centre of design, business, media and education. The *away* has moved from a myth to the marketplace, which is to say that waste is no longer 'waste', but instead has been reimagined as a 'resource', an 'asset', a 'nutrient' and an 'opportunity'. Corporate marketing campaigns claim that waste is now 'beautiful', and that waste is no longer a 'problem' – rather, it is the 'solution'. I've heard people talk about waste as a 'trend to design into' and other people call circularity the 'waste-to-gold' revolution. When so much of the fashion industry runs on a business model that extracts finite resources to produce an infinite amount of stuff, any conversation about recycling waste feels like progress. If we could just turn that stuff back into resources, then everything would be fine – right? It's not so simple. Waste and greed are two sides of the same destructive path. This means that waste cannot be revolutionised without a greater reckoning and reconciliation. And I don't see much reckoning. What I see is a mass depoliticisation of waste.

THE CONTEXT

I think about and 'deal' with clothing waste on a daily basis. Since 2016, my not-for-profit has been working with second-hand clothing retailers and upcyclers in Accra's Kantamanto Market through our project called Dead White Man's Clothes. Kantamanto is one of the largest resale and upcycling economies in the world. It is a vibrant, bustling hub of what the Global North now calls sustainability. It is also a mess.

In Kantamanto, 30,000 people work six days a week to sell, repair, clean and upcycle the Global North's clothing waste. This should be applauded, but it should not be romanticised. These 30,000 people take on a level of risk that is unjust. Many of Kantamanto's retailers take out loans with thirty-five per cent interest rates to purchase the bales of clothing that have been shipped from all over the world – clothing that has, in most cases, been donated for free by consumers or collected by brands as deadstock write-offs. With only twenty per cent of Kantamanto's retailers making a profit, many refer to their business as a 'gambling job'. On top of the steep financial risk associated with this business, the labour is physically back-breaking and spiritually dehumanising.

AND THEN THERE IS THE WASTE

Roughly 15 million garments flow through Kantamanto Market on a weekly basis. Kantamanto's ecosystem of retailers, dyers, printers, cleaners, tailors and upcyclers recommodify exponentially more clothing than any 'modern', technology-enabled resale platform in the Global North. For comparison, thredUp's 2020 report states that they have 'recirculated' (an unclear term) 100 million items total and 4 million 'fast-fashion' items since thredUp began as a business in 2009. Kantamanto recirculates (in this case, meaning rehabilitates and resells) 100 million items – the overwhelming majority of them 'fast-fashion' – every four months. But unlike resale platforms like thredUp, there is no outlet for the clothing that Kantamanto cannot sell. If our clothing lives within a linear economy, then Kantamanto is the end of the line. Not only is there nowhere for unsold clothing to go after Kantamanto, but for Kantamanto retailers, there is nothing even resembling the hundreds of millions of dollars of investment that thredUp, and similar platforms, have received.

Despite the best efforts of Kantamanto's entrepreneurs, forty per cent of the clothing leaves the market as waste. Accra lacks the landfill space for this clothing waste, so much of it is burned in the open air, swept into the gutter from where it eventually makes its way to the sea or dumped in informal settlements where Accra's most vulnerable citizens live. I have worked alongside waste pickers clawing through garbage in hopes of finding valuable materials and I have washed human faeces off of clothing recovered from landfill – clothing that was manufactured by some of the world's largest and most profitable brands and that was sent to Ghana in the name of diversion and circularity. Waste is not an abstract concept to me and that waste is all the more real for the people who work in Kantamanto day in and day out, playing a game that they cannot win.

A 'GOLDMINE'

I remember the first time a brand referred to our research findings as a 'goldmine'. They were talking about the waste from Kantamanto. Hearing this from one of the largest fashion brands on the planet and from a member of their sustainability team, no less, sent my heart into my gut. It confirmed the fears that had provoked my not-for-profit to launch Dead White Man's Clothes (and to name our project as such) in 2016, while simultaneously making me wonder if sharing it so publicly would end up doing more harm than good. This is a company, the leaders of which hoard wealth gained by exploiting the labour power of disenfranchised women who work in garment factories. This is a company that has no trouble projecting sales across dozens of different countries and cultures while claiming that a living wage for garment workers is simply incalculable. A company that uses its massive marketing apparatus to prey on the insecurities of young people, making them believe that consumption will solve their problems. A company that relies on disposability to grow with godlike limitlessness. For this company (and others since then) to call Kantamanto's waste stream a 'goldmine' isn't merely absurd. It's violent.

For our Ghanaian team members, the word 'goldmine' stings. It evokes an immediate connection to the Gold Coast Colony – a name given to many diverse West African nations by foreigners. It is a phrase that speaks to the historical exploitation of mineral resources and of human life. Heard within the word 'goldmine' is also the specific ongoing environmental and human cost of small-scale gold mining called *galamsey*, the politics of which are entangled with the current neocolonial scramble for Africa. It is a reminder that little has changed since the recent time of formal colonisation. The minds of foreigners are still capable of collapsing all the richness that Ghana represents into an extraction site for foreign benefit.

Personally, when I hear 'goldmine' the first image that comes to my mind is of a baby boy. I don't trust the internet to respect intimate details, so we will call this baby boy 'O'. O's mum had worked as a kayayo in Kantamanto. This is a job that requires head-carrying large, heavy bales of imported second-hand clothing throughout the market, often travelling a mile (1.6 kilometres) or more between importers and retailers. As a kayayo, her labour fuels the Kantamanto economy, which, again, is one of the largest reuse, resale and upcycling economies in the world. Her labour does not afford the luxury of childcare, so O had to go to work with his mum. She carried him wrapped around her back while also carrying 120 lbs (54 kg) of clothing compressed into a bale on her head. O's mom was careful, as all kayayei are, to walk steady with a straight neck and a hand holding the side of her bale. But as she turned to carry the clothing up a flight of stairs, the narrow and uneven steps threw off her balance. The bale fell backwards onto O, crushing his skull.

When we met, O's dad pulled out his mobile phone to show me photos of his baby boy's body – photos you expect to see when researching armed conflict, not when researching second-hand clothing. O's mom couldn't speak about what happened. She blames herself.

You might be wondering if O's story is an anomaly. It's not. Mohammed Salifu, the director of the Kayayei Youth Association, carries the weight of many stories like this. Babies who have died. Children whose limbs have been crushed by bales. Kayayei, whose necks have broken under the weight of the clothing they carry, falling dead in the street.

I want to pause here to honour the horrific nature of what I just shared with you and to clarify what it is that we are talking about. The bale that crushed and killed O was composed of deadstock from brands (including returns) and of second-hand clothing that was unwanted by citizens of the Global North.

Thinking that their clothes will find a second life with someone who needs the thing that they no longer want, most people have truly kind – however naive – intentions when they donate clothing. Most people believe that the clothes they donate will be kept out of landfill. Clothing donations are billed as socially positive and environmentally sustainable. And now, many companies are marketing their own take-back clothing-collection programmes as the green way to shop for new clothes, often rewarding consumers with an in-store credit for dropping off their old clothes in their bins. But the purported sustainability of the global second-hand clothing trade is founded on the deficit myth. It is true that there is too much clothing in the Global North, but it is not true that there is a deficit of clothing in the Global South.

The truth is that most of what ends up in Kantamanto is donated simply because fast-fashion requires turnover, not attachment. Fast fashion isn't made to be loved, to be kept, to be cared for. Clothing is donated because there is a never-ending supply of new clothing to replace it. The second-hand trade is the outlet necessary for the first-hand trade to exist. Few people understand this because there is almost zero transparency or traceability in the second-hand supply chain. What you may know as 'second hand' is the primary supply chain for millions of human beings, including millions of Ghanaian citizens. If there were transparency and traceability, we would understand that the ethics of second hand are not so simple. Clothing donations, collection, sorting, exporting, importing and resale is a big business reaching nearly every corner of the globe in the same way that the creation of new, first-hand clothes does; one industry does not exist without the other. Second-hand clothing is part of the fashion industry. The fact that we – consumers, fashion-industry advocates and even second-hand clothing exporters – know so little about the 'afterlife' of our donations speaks to our priorities and underscores the colonial legacy of second-hand markets. The story of Kantamanto is not something new; rather, for decades it has been both intentionally hidden and unintentionally overlooked thanks to the implicit bias of those, myself included, who are complicit in upholding and advancing white supremacy. And only now, as the conversation around circularity has become embedded within a fashion industry seeking to rebrand itself as green, does the story of Kantamanto's overflowing waste seem relevant to the brands searching for their next 'goldmine'.

This has everything to do with profit and nothing to do with impact: a clothing company that calls itself 'circular' while continuing to overproduce is not interested in solving the problem – it is interested in extracting profit from the problem. While 'goldmine' might roll off the tongue as a seemingly benign corporatism, it is insulting and painful for those who have been doing the work. It is insulting to the Ghanaian designers who have been upcycling and using deadstock because second-hand clothing is the only material available to them now that the second-hand clothing trade has decimated their local textile economy. It's insulting to the thousands of retailers who clean, iron, dye, sort and clip threads from our unwashed donations. And to the *kayayei* who transport clothing from here to there and back again, over and over and over, literally risking their lives so that each garment has a shot at another life. 'Goldmine' isn't just a word – it is an attitude and orientation towards the world. Another phrase comes to mind: it takes money to make money. In many ways, this is the pervasive motto of capitalism, implying that the people willing and able to risk the most financial capital can reap the most rewards. But what about the people risking the most human capital? We need to reckon with the fact that the people who shoulder the most risk are not the people with the most secure profit stream, and that the companies now calling waste beautiful are the companies that have never dealt with the ugly truth of waste. A materials economy in which waste is considered a resource is not revolutionary if this system continues to operate within a global economy built on colonial trade routes, extractive capitalism and a growth imperative. This model will substitute waste for raw resources, but it will do so in a way that takes us down the same destructive path that we have been on.

JUSTICE

We have to be explicit about what we want for the future of fashion. I don't want to turn waste into 'gold'. I want the waste dumped in Ghana to be recovered so that soil can be regenerated to support food sovereignty and so that free, clean drinking water can flow. I don't want the waste to be recovered so that clothing can be turned into more clothing. There is a difference. Justice will not be the inevitable by-product of take-back programmes, clothing donations or recycling technology. Fashion's waste crisis is the result of compounded exploitation. Without a concerted effort, circularity does nothing to address the colonial legacies on which the prevailing fashion industry is built. In fact, by decoupling resource constraints from corporate growth, circularity could turn even more of the world into a corporate colony. But it doesn't have to.

Firstly, we must talk about production quantities and then we must reduce them. There is too much clothing in the world. This is not a radical opinion. It is a fact. I've seen the end of fashion's linear economy and it is literally overflowing into the ocean. As a global society, we do not need more clothing. Any brand that says otherwise is delusional or outright lying. Many independent brands speak openly about this but Big Fashion does not. Brands should be required to publish information about how many units they produce of each item that they sell. Journalists should ask questions about production volumes, and media outlets should illustrate the excessive scale of production in the same way that some clever people have illustrated the mind-boggling difference between median income and billionaire wealth. As advocates like Aja Barber have said, we can no longer divorce scale from impact.

Secondly, we must redistribute wealth; this can come in many forms. After all, a circle is inherently redistributive. The Circular Economy, as promoted by the titans of linear industries, has been ripe for greenwashing because it is a materials-based framework with little mention of people and no mention of capital. As a result, brands launch take-back programmes before they pay an actual living wage. In fact, it seems as though the companies investing the most in the circular economy are also the most likely to be exploiting garment workers. We should also illustrate the gap between garment-worker pay and CEO earnings and stop giving centre stage to the people who are openly exploiting thousands of others for personal gain. With wages so low and environmental consequences externalised, clothing is so disposable that store returns are not worth restocking and are instead landfilled or diverted into the second-hand economy. Through the prevailing model of the fashion industry, brands are invested in disposability. Paying garment workers a living wage is not only just, it is perhaps the most accessible mechanism we have to catalyse a divestment from overproduction. There are several possible legal mechanisms that could accelerate the living-wage prerogative. By way of example, I suggest looking at some of the recent initiatives around which the #PayUp Movement is organising.

Another form of wealth distribution is eco-reparations and equitable investments in communities like Kantamanto that have been trying to clean up fashion's mess for decades. The people who live in proximity to the problem are also closest to the solutions. The Global North loves to talk in circles, debating the legitimacy of the word 'sustainability' while the people who labour day in and day out in Kantamanto have been doing sustainability. Let's prioritise Kantamanto's work to create a Circular Economy, not that of the people who have benefited most from the linear economy. It bears repeating that Kantamanto is among the largest resale/reuse/recommerce/upcycling platforms/ economies in the world. We should invest in it as such – not as a goldmine for extractive corporate interests, but as a place of real impact for a future we all share. Make less stuff, move money and decentralise power. There can be no 'sustainable innovation' without justice. Waste will either be the next frontier of colonialism and greenwashing or waste will serve as an opportunity for greater reckoning and reparation. Choose the latter.

Originally published on Atmos.earth
Learn more about Kantamanto at theor.org

BEYOND THE ECONOMY
OF WASTE
Kate Soper

All living creatures reproduce, consume and excrete – and many of them also leave behind constructions that survive them. Yet none of the organic matter created, for example, by the estimated 10 billion billion ants on the planet properly counts as waste since all of it is recycled and thus returned to nature. It is only humans who create waste in the sense of an unused or unusable and persisting – and often toxic – residue of their productive activity and consumption, and even they have only done so on any serious scale in relatively recent times. But so specific has waste become to human societies today that it might now qualify as a major distinguishing marker between our species and the rest of nature.

Industrialisation has been the driving factor in this process – and the richer and more developed a society has become, the more rubbish it has created. Today, sixteen per cent of the global population consumes eighty per cent of the world's resources, and waste now accounts for the majority of material flows in the creation of this affluent lifestyle. In a study of some of the wealthiest OECD (Organisation for Economic Co-operation and Development) countries, it was found that between fifty-five and seventy-five per cent of the total materials requirement in those countries took the form of resources discarded in the processes of production.[1] Secondary or post-consumption residue is of the same order, as anyone who has visited a waste tip or passed by an incinerator or landfill site will be well aware. A significant part of this total comprises goods that have scarcely been used, or have proved surplus to requirements or otherwise unfit for sale. Although world hunger is on the rise, nearly a third of food production annually is lost or thrown away.[2] In the UK, it is estimated that some £30 billion-worth of unused clothing hangs in wardrobes and eleven million items go to landfill each week. Worldwide, 100 billion items of clothing are made annually, with brands shovelling excess production into incinerators.[3] Amazon, we have learned, has been doing much the same with millions of unsold TVs, laptops and other electronic items.[4] The built-in obsolescence and rapid turnover of the hi-tech goods that do get sold has now made discarded electronics the fastest-growing form of waste across the Western world. It is also the most complex: a fingernail-sized microchip may contain more than half the elements on the periodic table.[5] In the resulting salvage industry that has evolved in some of the poorest parts of the globe, the scavenging workers (many of them children) melt circuit boards to release valuable chips – and highly toxic fumes. Plastics are either burned or jettisoned, creating polluting ash and other residues that poison surrounding land and waterways. The statistics on waste are so dystopian, and the images of its dumping grounds so desolate, that it is hard to credit they could be justified in any form of economic accounting, least of all in an era facing environmental collapse. But justified it certainly is, in effect, by all those – politicians across the left/right divide, mainstream economists, most of the media and much of the electorate as well – who unquestioningly support economic growth and regard GDP (Gross Domestic Product) as the key measure of progress and prosperity.[6] For waste is intrinsic to growth and growth is dependent on its production: the smaller the volume of goods produced, and the more serviceable and durable they prove, the less readily they are discarded and the less waste is produced. But as sales dwindle, so profits decline and growth shrinks. Capitalism in this respect abhors sustainable production.

Designers are implicated in troubling ways in this contradiction between the growth imperative and that of sustainable living. The summons to which they want to respond in their concern for the environment is to design for longevity and minimal waste. Yet they remain answerable for much of their employment to an economic system that demands frequent turnover and regular disposal of goods – and hence calls for some form of obsolescence in design, whether in the material construction of the product or its compliance with fast-fashion.

However, designers who are alert to this contradiction and chafing at it are also well placed to contribute to the evolution of an alternative ethos and aesthetic of production. As is well represented in this book, many are already involved in the development of 'zero-waste' or circular-design methods of production that give priority to 'upcycling' over recycling – in other words, to the minimisation of residue and closed-loop cycles of resource use. The ultimate aim here is to eliminate from the original production process any resources that are neither ultimately biodegradable nor reusable to maximum extent in other production processes.

Even this revolution in materials productivity, however, may remain caught in the more abiding tensions between free-market expansion and ecological conservation through its reliance on the kind of goods that it seeks to supersede. Car tyres may be ground into crumb for basketball courts, but the recycled waste remains locked into a compromised form of consumption. What is also needed are real reductions by the richest countries in energy use, and hence the production and the consumption of material goods: a transition from the growth-driven to a 'doughnut' form of economy that is committed to remaining within the bounds of a globally just and sustainable use of resources. In her influential *Doughnut Economics*, Kate Raworth argues for a regenerative and distributive economy that meets the essential needs of those without provision for them, while remaining within the ecological boundaries upon which all life depends. Such an economy is represented by an area between two rings (hence the 'doughnut' image) considered as the safe and just space for humanity.[7]

By fostering an altered aesthetic response to the material culture of consumerism, design could play a key role in challenging the monopoly exercised by advertising over current conceptions of gratification and the 'good life', and thus help to further public support for this green renaissance. In doing so, it would engage, as advertising long has, with the close dependencies between our ethical beliefs about and our aesthetic responses to the world. If, for example, you come to know that a product does you harm, you tend to perceive it differently. Hence the need for cigarette advertisement, until it was finally banned in the UK, to be emptied of any imagery of actual smoking, or the reliance of car promotion on an implausible depiction of the vehicle as travelling in isolation, unaffected by the congestion of any other traffic. A green renaissance in the cultural politics of design would harness this interdependency of belief and aesthetic experience for its own counter-consumerist purposes. It would also seek to extend it to the environment at large. Through being rejected or negatively represented, goods that were unsustainable in their function or design, even though not responsible for any immediate personal damage, would cease to exercise their one-time aesthetic compulsion. Likewise, forms of life that were previously perceived as enticingly glamorous would come gradually to be viewed as cumbersome, ugly and retrograde thanks to their association with noise and toxicity, and their legacy of unrecyclable waste.[8]

It is true, of course, that were this distaste to prevail, it would not be very good for business. But this approach holds out much more promise of avoiding the descent into ecological barbarism than continuing with business as usual.

THE SCALE OF THE PROBLEM

There is no waste in nature, yet our planet is
drowning in humanity's pollution. Swelling streams
of discarded plastics, textiles, electronics and
materials from construction, agriculture and industry
are overwhelming the systems set up to manage them.
In the UK, most of our rubbish is incinerated or
buried. The rest is exported to other countries,
out of sight but still wreaking damage on people
and the land. Rising levels of waste are fuelled
by our increasing and careless consumption.
We have reached peak waste.

Waste contributes to climate change through the
production of greenhouse gases. Human activity,
including burning oil and gas in factories, heating
our homes, emissions from vehicles and planes,
and dumping waste in landfill, produces carbon
dioxide or methane, gases that are causing the
Earth's temperature to rise. Higher temperatures
lead to melting icecaps, which cool the oceans and
cause rising sea levels. These, in turn, lead to
extreme weather, affecting vulnerable communities
and species.

1   Opposite: Oxford Tire
    Pile # 1, Westley,
    California, 1999.
    Archival pigment print

2   Below: Lithium Mines
    #1, Salt Flats, Atacama
    Desert, Chile, 2017.
    Archival pigment print

3   Overleaf: Chuquicamata
    Copper Mine Overburden
    #2, Calama, Chile, 2017.
    Archival pigment print

Engaging the viewer in the environmental debate, the
work of Canadian photographer Edward Burtynsky captures
the sublime quality of the unseen industrial landscape.
His bird's-eye views reveal the impact of human activity
on the natural world, from vast landfill sites that
show piles of plastic and expose the scale of our waste
production, to enormous open scars where rare earth
minerals are mined for the manufacture of our devices
and batteries. These four photographs from Burtynsky's
series *Oil and Anthropocene* show 'the indelible marks
left by humankind on the geological face of our planet'.

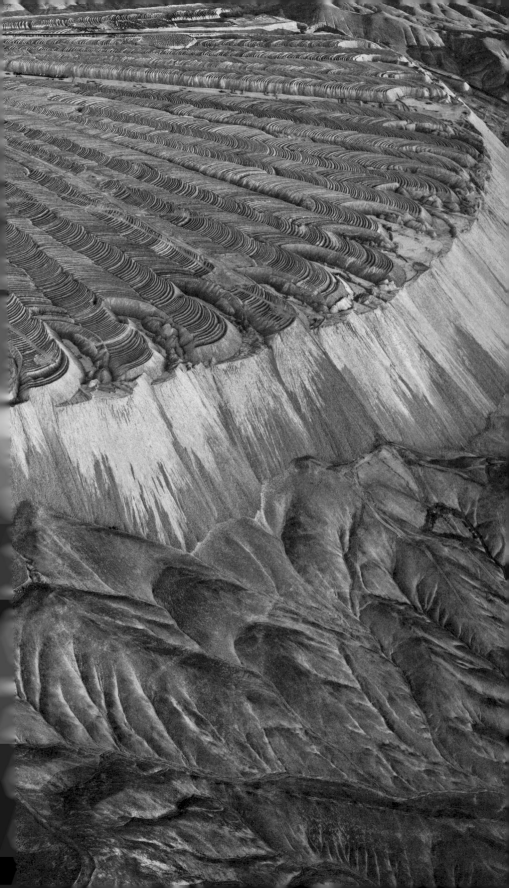

1 Dandora Landfill #3,
Plastics Recycling,
Nairobi, Kenya, 2016.
Archival pigment print

These plastic pebbles or 'plastiglomerates' wash
up on beaches from Hawaii to Orkney. They form when
plastic bottles or other plastic waste that have been
thrown on a bonfire or melted by the sun combine with
sand, shingle, seaweed and other natural debris. First
identified by the oceanographer Charles Moore in 2006
and later given the name plastiglomerates by Dr Patricia
Corcoran and Kelly Jazvac in 2014, plastiglomerates have
come to represent the moment when human pollution and
nature permanently fused. The plastiglomerates in these
images were collected on beaches in Cornwall by the
volunteers of the Cornish Plastic Pollution Coalition.

HOW WE MADE A
THROWAWAY CULTURE

The glamour of the 'throwaway' emerged out of
the prosperity of the post-war period. In the
1950s, mass production and cheap materials reduced
the cost of things. However, time and labour were
increasingly expensive, making repairs no longer
time- or cost-effective. Products were made for
convenience, with disposable cups, cutlery and
nappies easier to replace than to clean, reducing
the domestic workload. The range of materials it
was considered acceptable to throw away started with
paper and grew to include glass, ceramics, plastics,
tin, aluminium and, increasingly with fast fashion,
textiles. Boredom has replaced convenience, with 24
per cent of people who throw out clothing stating
they are sick of wearing the same things. In 2018,
300,000 tonnes of textiles ended up in landfill.
The UK generated 44kg of single-use plastic waste
per person in 2019. The COVID-19 pandemic led to
a record surge in plastic waste – from disposable
protective equipment to single-use plastic packaging
– due to health and hygiene concerns.

In August 1955, *LIFE* magazine published a short article
called 'Throwaway Living', accompanied by the image
shown here. It is considered one of the earliest uses
of the phrase 'throwaway living'.

Making the scene everywhere—new porcelain-smooth Scott Cups.

New and very in!
The party 'glass' you just enjoy...
and throw away.

Scott Cups!

Now—a new kind of party glass made of miracle polystyrene. Drinks taste great in them. Like glass. They're lip-smooth like glass. Ice clinks in them. Like glass.

No washups, no storage—and no problems with broken glassware. In sociable-size packs of 20 and 40—for your next party.

SCOTT (S) MAKES IT BETTER FOR YOU

1 Opposite: Advertisement
   for Scott Cups Party
   Glass, 1965

2 Below: Ralphs plastic
   bag, 1980s

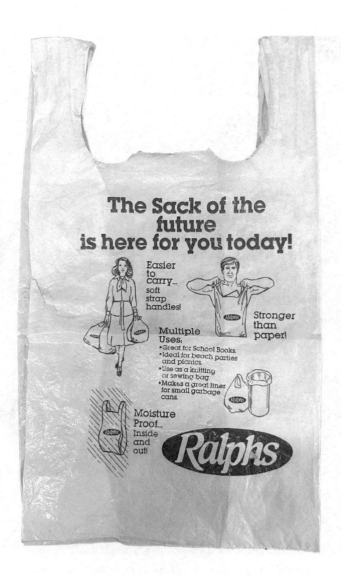

One of the earliest brands of disposable cup, Dixie
Cups, was established in the USA in 1907. The cup was
designed by a lawyer who was concerned about spreading
germs through shared glasses. By 1955, they were
marketed simply for convenience and leisure.

Since the 1980s pieces of orange plastic have regularly
been washing up on beaches in France. Years later, they
were discovered to be fragments of Garfield telephones
escaping from a lost shipping container that had become
lodged deep in an inaccessible cave. In 2015, it was
estimated that between 4.8 million and 12.7 million
tonnes of plastic enter the ocean each year. Larger
pieces degrade, becoming microplastics that enter
the food chain.

1   Garfield phone pieces.
    Collected by the
    association Ar Viltansoù
    on the beaches of
    Conquet and Plougonvelin
    (Finistère, France),
    2017–21

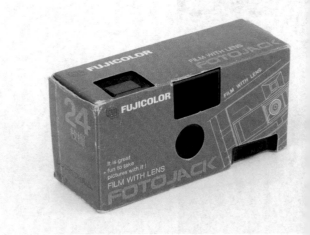

Plastic cutlery was reintroduced on aeroplanes as a
safety precaution after the 9/11 terrorist attacks.
Throwaway culture is often influenced by global events,
as with the COVID-19 pandemic and the dramatically
increased use of disposable face masks.

1 Opposite: Ekco
cutlery, 1970. Design:
David Harmen Powell;
manufacture: Ekco
Plastics Ltd

2 Opposite: Fujicolour
Fotojack film,
Fujifilm Corp.

3 Below: Sensor
Excel shaver, 1993.
Design: Dieter Rams;
manufacture: Gillette

4 Below: Cristal Fine
biro, 1995. Marcel Bich,
Société BiC

WHY DO WE
LOVE PLASTIC?

A synthetic polymer, plastic is an extraordinary
material: lightweight, malleable, waterproof and
durable. It can be solid and made bright with colour
or produced as a delicate, transparent film. Easy
to mass manufacture, plastic makes many everyday
essentials inexpensive. Whether preserving our
food or reducing cross-contamination in medicine,
use of plastic – from syringes, crash helmets,
drink bottles or credit cards to cars, office
chairs, waterproof jackets and mobile phones
– has transformed our lives.

Plastic is a high-grade material made from
virgin crude oil, and it lasts from 450 years to
forever. Originally intended to replace ivory and
tortoiseshell, today its widest use is in packaging.
Of the 359 million tonnes of plastic produced
globally each year, 40 per cent is used just once.
Much gets washed into our oceans, where it is eaten
by fish and seabirds, finding its way into the human
food chain. Microparticles have even been found in
the placenta of unborn babies. We need to rethink
how and when we use plastic.

1 Opposite: Model 1000
Bullet portable radio,
1946. FADA Radios

2 Below: 4867 Universale
stacking chair, 1968.
Injection-moulded
polypropylene and
rubber. Design: Joe
Colombo; manufacture:
Kartell S.p.A., Italy

1 Opposite: Wonderlier Tupperware container, about 1950. Design: Earl Silas Tupper; manufacture: Tupperware Plastics Co.

2 Opposite: Extra Air bicycle helmet, 1993. Plastic (polycarbonate and polystyrene). Manufacture: Specialized

3 Below: Black ST/201 television, 1969. Designed by Marco Zanuso and Richard Sapper for Brionvega, Italy

4 Below: Long Reach Can, watering can, 1991. Plastic (PVC). Manufacture: Plysu

BUILT TO BREAK

Lightbulbs were originally designed to last for up
to 2,500 hours. Then, on 23 December 1924, the Phoebus
cartel ruled that they should last just 1,000 hours,
artificially halving their lifespan and forcing
consumers to buy more replacements. The cartel fined
manufacturers if their lightbulbs lasted too long.
Phoebus consisted of major international lightbulb
manufacturers, including Germany's Osram, Philips
from the Netherlands and the USA's General Electric.
It is often credited with introducing the strategy
now known as 'planned obsolescence'.

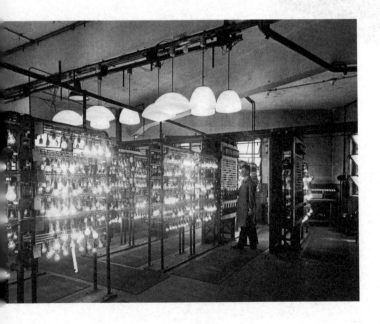

Samples being checked at a testing facility of Philips,
the Netherlands, to ensure they conform to the shorter
lifetime standards set by the Phoebus cartel.

1   Below: Livermore
    Centennial Light, 1901.
    Manufacture: Shelby
    Electric Company

This lightbulb has been glowing almost continuously
for more than one million hours (about 120 years). First
installed in 1901 in the Livermore Fire Department,
California, it has only ever been switched off a handful
of times. Declared the oldest known working lightbulb
by *The Guinness Book of World Records* in 1972, the
Centennial Bulb is proof that well-designed products
can last more than a lifetime.

'Planned Obsolescer

YES! SAYS BROOKS STEVENS

"PLANNED OBSOLESCENCE" results from the consumer's desire to own something a little newer, a little better, a little sooner than is necessary. The term was first used, I believe, six years ago in a talk I made before the Minneapolis Advertising Club on the subject of industrial design.

The normal desire in times of prosperity to satisfy one's ego with that which is the *best* as well as the newest is a fact that business can depend upon.

There is also another definition of planned obsolescence from the manufacturer's standpoint. Any successful business depends upon production, sales, and profit. This situation is also tied directly to employment. Therefore, it is not only the goal but the

The industrial designer's first obligation is to hi client, then to the economy. The consumer obviou ly benefits in a higher standard of living and in hi own choice of purchase when and if he pleases.

The designer must anticipate future demand. Th average consumer product requires from six to nir months in tooling, and in the automobile field th lead time may be 18 months. The industrial designe is called upon to be working from a year to two yea ahead of that particular article which may be enjo ing booming acceptance at the moment.

It is interesting to note that in April, 1958, th eminent U. S. financial columnist Sylvia Porter p forth the question as to whether planned obsole

duty of every manufacturer to engage in continual research and product development to provide continually the market with the best and the newest.

And what of the standpoint of the designer—the man whose planning causes obsolescence? The designer should basically be a businessman, engineer, and stylist, in that order.

He is not a fine artist producing works for exhibition only.

The stylist percentage of the industrial designer is the relationship of art to industry.

Art for art's sake is not salable in the market place of consumer goods.

cence was an evil or a boon. It is significant beca this particular month was probably the pinnac the United States' most recent "conversational re sion." I call it this because of its relatively s duration and because of the fact that Americans able to snowball verbally a situation which h tendency to be unpleasant or discouraging. This begun six months before with the introductic the 1958 Detroit-built automobiles. The usua design and styling magic had at long last cast a note and the ready consumer had decided to be a "looker" and not a buyer.

It is conceivable that we [*Continued on pag*

An industrial designer of Milwaukee, Wis., Brooks Stevens entered the field in 1933 after graduation from Cornell University. His firm, Brooks Stevens Associates, has more than 100 manufacturing firms as clients. He is one of the original Fellows of the Society of Industrial Designers, was a Rotarian for many years, has four children.

Do manufacturers deliberately lead
on in the race to "keep up with the
Do they deliberately design new goo
chief purpose of making consumer
with last year's perfectly good but

12

s It Fair?

NO! SAYS WALTER DORWIN TEAGUE

PEOPLE have an allergy to being gypped. We in the U. S. have several examples lately of their energetic reaction when it dawns on them that their friendly confidence has been betrayed.

We went all out for the big money quiz shows so long as sealed envelopes delivered by vice-presidents of banks seemed to guarantee that they were on the level. But since we learned, reluctantly, that the massive productions were rigged, our revulsion has been massive and catastrophic—to the programs, the participants, the networks, and the sponsors.

In the same way the most popular disc jockeys passed instantly into oblivion when their fans (and their curiously unobservant employers) learned that

seen by any unprejudiced eyes: people in large numbers simply didn't like the typical American cars they were offered. Yes, these people had cash and credit both, they went on buying other things, their savings accounts zoomed. They bought small foreign cars as fast as they could get delivery, and especially they bought the little Volkswagen, about the smallest, most economical, sturdiest, and least pretentious of the lot. Also the Volkswagen scarcely changes its body style from one decade to another. In 1959 a total of 600,000 foreign cars have been sold in the U.S.A., and exports of American cars have dropped sadly.

During the slump the lone pioneer American

they had been selecting records for plugging under payola incentives.

A much more hurtful instance of public reaction happened a couple of years ago to the automobile industry, when Americans refrained in astonishing numbers from buying new automobiles. The sales curve took such a bender that it brought on a minor depression, since the health of this most important American industry affects the welfare of hundreds suppliers of parts, materials, and services, many of them huge industries themselves.

You can try every way you like to explain away this buyers' strike, but the facts were plain to be

maker of small, unpretentious cars has had to multiply his production capacity several times and has seen his shares advance since early 1958 from 8 or 9 to 80 or 90 on the New York Stock Exchange.

If you inquired around, you got a variety of answers all adding up to similar conclusions:

"They're hideous."

"They're too big, too hard to park, and they won't fit in my garage."

"I don't like those silly fins, nor all that chrome gook, nor those lights hung like bunches of grapes fore and aft."

"They eat gas and it costs [Continued on page 57]

and wouldn't it be better if people spent money for other things? Or are new designs better designs that stimulate buying and economy? In this debate-of-the-month, two designers give their views.—THE EDITORS.

Walter Dorwin Teague, first president of the Society of Industrial Designers, began his career in 1907 as an artist, entered industrial design in 1926. He has designed autos, cameras, furniture, appliances, exhibits, etc., has authored several books, in 1939 received the American Design Award. He heads Walter Dorwin Teague Associates of New York City.

In the 1960s, the ethics of 'planned obsolescence' were debated by designers, consumers and manufacturers. Here, Clifford Brooks Stevens, who popularised the term, and Walter Dorwin, a designer and writer, consider the pros and cons of building things to break, looking at job retention, economic value and the obligations designers have to consumers and society.

COMMISSION: FADAMA 40, IBRAHIM MAHAMA

The artist Ibrahim Mahama, based in Tamale, Ghana, has created a new work (*Fadama 40*, 2021) exposing the dumping of European electronic waste in his country. Much of this used to end up at Agbogbloshie in Accra, a vast scrapyard and marketplace for processing and trading e-waste. One common but toxic practice was the burning of electrical cables to remove the plastic insulation from the wires, so the copper could be reclaimed. Mahama has used this copper to create new frames for the TVs in this media wall (see p. 6).

Agbogbloshie's complex community of scrap dealers,
recyclers and makers provided economic opportunities,
but working conditions were hazardous and the site
created chronic air and water pollution. In July 2021,
the Ghanaian government closed down sections of the
dump and relocated the scrap dealers to a new site.

GLOBAL ELECTRONIC WASTE

Global electronic waste generation totalled more
than 50 million metric tonnes in 2019 and is expected
to increase by an estimated 20 million metric tonnes
in the coming decade. E-waste is the fastest-growing
waste stream worldwide.

2019

2029

FOOD WASTE

1.3 billion tonnes of food are estimated to be wasted
globally each year; approximately one-third or half of
all food produced for human consumption is wasted.

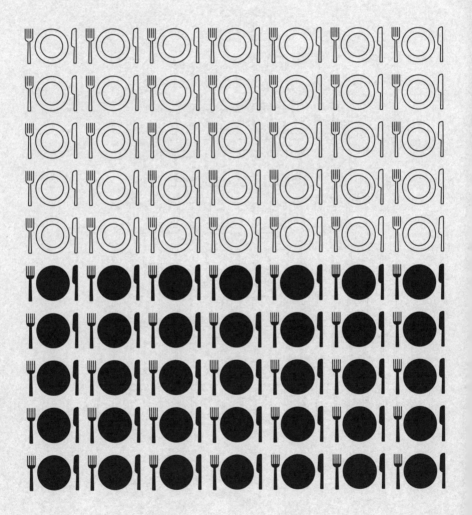

HOW MUCH RUBBISH IS RECLAIMED?

Over 2 billion metric tonnes of rubbish is produced
annually; only 15 per cent of that is reclaimed.

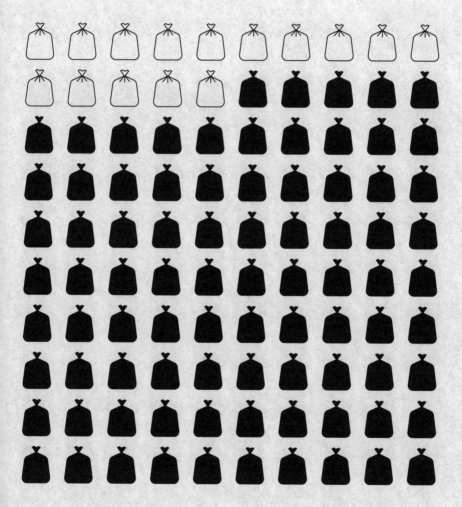

TEXTILE WASTE

Europeans use nearly 26 kilos of textiles per person,
and discard about 11 kilos of them every year. 87 per
cent of clothing ends up in landfills or incinerators.

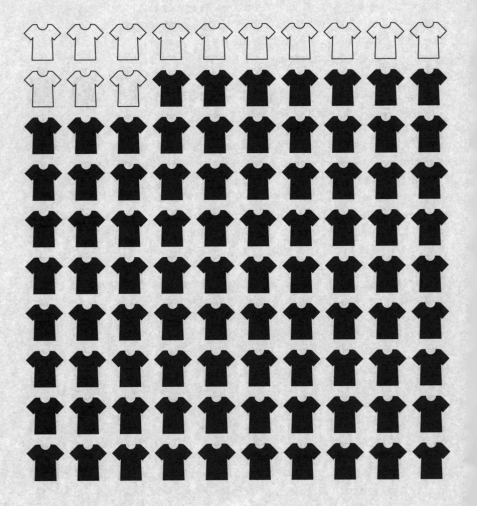

A HIERARCHY FOR DEALING WITH WASTE

PREVENTION

Using less material in design and manufacture. Keeping products for longer; reuse. Using less hazardous materials.

PREPARING FOR REUSE

Checking, cleaning, repairing, refurbishing whole items or spare parts.

RECYCLING

Turning waste into a new substance or product. Includes composting if it meets quality protocols.

OTHER RECOVERY

Includes anaerobic digestion, incineration with energy recovery, gasification and prolysis to produce energy and materials.

DISPOSAL

Landfill and incineration without energy recovery.

WASTE GENERATION BY INCOME LEVEL

5% Low Income
29% Low-Mid Income
32% Upper-Mid Income
34% High Income

100%

KEY MOMENTS IN THE HISTORY OF PLASTIC PRODUCTION, 1930S–50S

	1933	Polyethylene is discovered (goes commercial in 1939)
	1935	Nylon is patented by Carothers and DuPont
	1936	Aircraft canopies are first produced in Perspex
	1937	Polystyrene
	1940	First production of PVC in UK
	1941	The first pilot plant is built for polytetrafluoroethylene (PTFE); it is marketed as 'Teflon'
1930s–1950s	1943	Teflon-polytetrafluroethylene (PTFE)
	1945	The production of LDPE the Sqezy bottle by Monsanto causes huge expansion in the use of plastic packaging instead of glass
	1947	Formica Melamine is introduced in the UK
	1948	Acrylonitrile-butadiene-styrene (ABS) is patented, and 12" long-playing records begin to be made in polyvinyl chloride (PVC)
	1949	Tupperware (made from polythylene) is launched in US
	1949	Lycra invented
	1950	Polyethylene bags first appear First polycarbonates produced

PLASTIC WASTE GENERATION BY INDUSTRIAL SECTOR, 2015

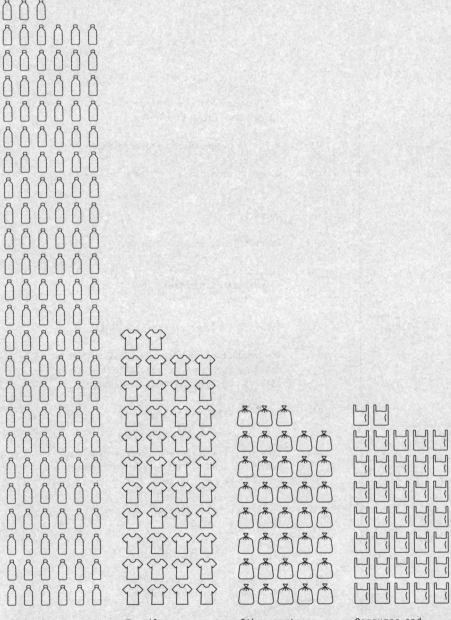

Packaging:
141 million
tonnes

Textiles:
42 million
tonnes

Other sectors:
38 million
tonnes

Consumer and
institutional
products:
37 million
tonnes

Transportation:
17 million tonnes

Electrical:
13 million tonnes

Construction:
13 million tonnes

Industrial
machinery:
1 million
tonnes

02 PRECIOUS WASTE

REPAIR CULTURE
Lee Vinsel

These days, I give a lecture in nearly all of my undergraduate courses titled 'Modernity = Cheap Crap'. My slides open with photographs of stuff overflowing from people's closets and garages. Nearly fifty per cent of American garages are used for storage to such a degree that you can no longer park a car in them. For a period, self-storage – spaces that you rent to put things you can't fit elsewhere – was one of the fastest-growing sectors in the United States.

Maybe the greatest excesses here stem from what we might call Ugly American Syndrome, but what I want to impress upon my students is how profoundly, for most people on this planet, human relationships with man-made objects have changed over the past two centuries. Mass production stands as one of the fundamental technological turning points in human history. It belongs in the pantheon of developments like agriculture, metal smelting, printing, electric power and modern concrete building.

To teach what the transformation of production means for our lives, I like to show students the documentary *Gunsmith of Williamsburg* (1969). The film follows an interpreter at Colonial Williamsburg – a museum that researches and recreates life in the American colonies – as he makes a rifle from scratch. It takes him a month. In 2019, a gunsmith at the museum told me that the starting price for rifles made there is $26,000 (the waiting list is several years long) and that cost doesn't even recoup their materials and work time. If you wanted to make a living from the things, you'd have to charge more. You can buy a new, factory-made rifle in a gun shop anywhere in the US for as little as $200.

Now apply that difference in price to nearly every human-made object around you, many of which obviously did not even exist 200 years ago and were certainly not made of the materials of which they are made today. In many ways, the everyday experiences of our lives are shaped, undergirded, made possible by these powers of mass production. Or as I put it, modernity equals cheap crap. Using production to drive down prices has had enormous impacts on life, which we take for granted. For example, eighty per cent of poor households in the US have air conditioning, not because welfare benefits have become more generous (they have not) but because the machines have become so inexpensive.

But these changes have also had enormous costs, especially for the environment. To become a mass-production culture is to become a waste culture. As historian of technology Rosalind

Williams describes, '[i]n some parts of the world, the basic garment of the common man went unchanged for centuries – the poncho in Peru, the dhoti in India, the long shirt in China, the kimono in Japan'.[1] Man-made objects took enormous quantities of specialised work; they were expensive and dear to those who held them. Objects were handed down from generation to generation. If they could be repaired, they were repaired. Old pieces of clothing that dwell in museums today are full of stitches, patches, little fixes that extended life.

By contrast, historian David Edgerton notes that it is more expensive to get a toaster repaired today than it is to buy a new one. The irony of Edgerton's statement is heightened when we consider the artist Thomas Thwaites' book and project *The Toaster*, in which he made a functional electric toaster from scratch. He found that the object he built cost 250 times what one in a store would go for. Would you get a toaster fixed if it cost $5,000? I bet you would. Mass production has transformed the way in which we value objects and make choices about them – including whether we put time and energy into maintaining and repairing them, into keeping them going or ... just throw them away.

Designers have played a central role in this overall process: they have been a part of mass production for over a century. Some judge General Motors (GM) to be one of the first modern corporations on the planet. Famously, GM hired designer Harley Earl, who previously had tricked out sweet rides for Hollywood movie stars, and created its 'Art and Color Section' in 1927. Design formally became one step in corporate product development just as GM President Alfred P. Sloan and other leaders were creating the annual model change and 'planned obsolescence'. As many have noted over the years, annual model changes are largely aesthetic – that is, design – matters. To stick with the automobile as our metaphor: the machine under the hood largely stays the same; it's the envelope and accessories that change. These small shifts are then heralded as earth-shattering in trade shows and advertisements. This tradition continues to this day when, for example, Apple Chief Executive Officer (CEO) Tim Cook walks on to a stage and announces that the new iPhone will come in Midnight Green in a tone of voice suggesting that Jesus Christ has just strolled through the door.

When it comes to maintenance and repair, there is actually a twin imperative – a contradiction – at the heart of capitalism and, thus, also for designers who, like engineers, are by and large servants of capital. On the one hand, corporations can and have made objects much more durable, maintainable and repairable over time. In the early days of the twentieth century, owning an automobile required that you could repair a car or be rich enough to hire a mechanic. Cars broke down constantly on the road. Tyres, batteries and other systems also required constant maintenance work. But, in large part because customers hankered for and even demanded it, corporations poured money and the cognitive resources of their employees into making their products easier to use and tougher by, for example, improving design and materials. Terms like 'maintainability' and professional fields like 'reliability engineering' took off in the post-Second World War period. The US appliance manufacturer Maytag created the character of the Maytag Man, used in advertisements off and on from 1967 to the present: the tagline was that the Maytag Man was 'the loneliest guy in town' because, the claim went, the company's machines were so durable and reliable that they never broke down.

On the other hand sit all disposable and poorly made things speeding their way to being interred under piles of earth – among other reasons, because corporations make profits by selling products over and over and over again. Since the Second World War, humans have reorganised the face of the planet to get the cheapest possible manufactured goods into international markets. Why would I bother fixing a lamp when I can buy a new, more fashionably up-to-date one for $15 while I'm picking up groceries at some big box store? Into the trash my bent or broken one goes. I've found it to be a kind of cliché or truism for designers proudly to point at all the objects in a room and mention that each article is – in a sense at least – designed. But now apply that insight, which is true enough, to all the things being vomited out of an overstuffed garage, items doomed to be buried in some landfill. Hmm. How should a designer feel about their ubiquity now?

Moreover, corporations have designed some things so that they simply cannot be either repaired or recycled. Kyle Wiens, the CEO of repair website iFixit and a leader of the Right to Repair Movement, once expressed frustration that Apple touted that its laptops were made of 'highly recyclable aluminum and glass'. He wrote, 'My friends in the electronics recycling industry tell me they have no way of recycling aluminum that has glass glued to it like Apple did with both [its laptops] and the recent iPad.'[2] My father-in-law is a chiropractor. One day, a motor on one of his adjusting tables failed. He called the manufacturer and they told him that they no longer supported that model because it was too old. When he took the motor to a local repairman who specialised in such machines, he was told that it was designed in such a way that it could not be repaired at all. If the manufacturer had come to fix the table, the serviceperson would have simply removed the old motor, inserted a new one and put the old one in the garbage.

Corporations – most famously, Apple and John Deere – have also used both physical and software-based designs to lock down repair and keep owners and independent repairpersons from fixing their products. Such barriers increase maintenance and repair costs, in terms of both time and money, and raise the likelihood that objects will become waste rather than being kept up.

We have also added bells and whistles to devices that make them die faster. When Andrew Russell and I were writing our book *The Innovation Delusion*, repair workers repeatedly told us that accessories like ice machines and water dispensers on refrigerators were the first things to go out. Now the trend is to add smart TVs and touchscreens to fridges. What could go wrong? We know what could go wrong, because adding microchips and computers to everyday technologies that have functioned perfectly well for decades without microchips and computers is one of the absolutely best ways to decrease their lifespans. Gay Gordon-Byrne, executive director of the repair trade association Repair.org and another leader of the Right to Repair movement, often tells people that the question 'Why are you putting a computer in that thing when it can work without one?' must become an environmental imperative.

Meanwhile, products – especially digital technologies, it turns out – are filled with non-renewable and non-recyclable resources. The European Chemical Society made an alternative periodic table showing the availability and vulnerability of the natural elements. It also visually represented which of the elements are put in smartphones. Several ofthose materials are under serious threat of running out in the next 100 years.

For all these reasons, it benefits the environment to keep our possessions going for as long as possible. For example, it takes less energy to charge and operate a smartphone for a decade than it does to build a new one. (There are exceptions to this rule: it is better to scrap even a new gasoline-powered automobile and buy an electric vehicle because cars produce their biggest environmental impact through energy use.) But long-lasting devices directly threaten corporate business models. We can see this concretely through something that happened at Apple in 2018–19: the company offered to replace batteries in its iPhones for only $29 after it was discovered that it had – without informing consumers that it was doing so – been throttling the speed of phones that used old batteries. Phone owners used the programme. Then Apple stock took a big hit when it failed to meet sales projections – in part because customers were, as Tim Cook explained in a letter, 'taking advantage of significantly reduced pricing for iPhone battery replacements'.[3] In other words, decreasing the price and, thereby, increasing the rate of repair had cut into expected sales.

      I firmly believe that corporations can improve the relationship between products, maintainability, recyclability and waste through voluntary action, but I believe even more strongly that the transformations that the Earth needs will require government regulation. Making objects long-lived simply cuts into corporate interests too much. My first book, *Moving Violations*, a history of US automobile regulation from 1890 to the present, examined the ways in which governments have used regulations to focus the corporate powers of innovation and design on socially beneficial, not merely profitable, technological change. We can and should turn these capacities of regulation towards making products more maintainable and durable.

      Sometimes the notion of 'circular economy' is helpful for thinking about these issues. The Ellen MacArthur Foundation, which has been the primary promoter of the concept, defines circular economy as 'gradually decoupling economic activity from consumption of finite resources, and designing waste out of the system'.[4] The idea can be reduced to three principles: 'design out waste and pollution, keep products and materials in use, and regenerate natural systems'.

      We can use these principles to regulate and then redesign products in order to make them last longer. Right to Repair laws that forbid companies from putting barriers on repair are a baseline requirement. The European Union's Right to Repair laws, which require products to be repairable for ten years, is a step in an even better direction, but we should go farther. If we set maintainability and recyclability standards very high – so high that they even exceed the current abilities of corporations to meet them – then companies will turn their capacities, including their Research and Development (R&D) labs, towards, and open up entirely new markets around, solving these problems. For example, where appropriate, products should include the kinds of new, more sustainable materials highlighted in this book. How do we design policy to generate not only the invention of such materials but also corporate take-up and diffusion of them? Moreover, repair cafés, tool libraries and other voluntary associations aimed at getting more people to repair their objects have their benefits, but nations following Sweden's example and offering tax benefits to incentivise repair would be much more effective. We must create policies that encourage people to take care of things, and support them in doing so.

To value the world is to act as a steward for – that is, to *look after* – it. In order to do this, we must also look after our things and make sure that they have long lives. To achieve these ends will absolutely require the power of the state. At times, I stand and watch modern society go by and doubt that we will ever find the political will to make these necessary changes.

AWAY FROM A NEW ARCHITECTURE
Barnabas Calder

1   Opposite: Viviano
Codazzi, *The Nativity
in an Ancient Ruin*,
c.1660. Oil on copper

The fall of ancient Rome in 410 CE has been widely accepted as the end of a great civilisation. As St Jerome saw it, 'the bright light of all the world was put out'.[1] How dared the Gothic barbarians destroy things of such beauty as the palaces, temples and fora of the Eternal City? How could they – and the centuries-worth of Rome-dwellers who followed them – tear apart such noble stones, loot the seating from the Colosseum, smash holes in ancient walls to bastardise them into crude farm buildings and cannibalise beautifully made antiquities into the walls of cruder medieval fortifications? What an unparalleled waste.

Yet in reality the modern world needs to learn urgent messages from these 'destructive' generations of Romans. Medieval Rome, shorn of its enormous imports of food from around the empire, was short of energy – fed and fuelled only by the food and firewood produced by local farmland. In these thin times, everything that was not in active use was available to be reused, and was reused. Unused buildings in the depopulated city became stockrooms of materials for new construction.

Showy metal components like the gilded bronze tiles of the Pantheon were obvious targets for removal – easy to recycle, and valuable. The lead from water pipes and roofs was another easy win. Marble cladding and giant column shafts of beautiful stone were coveted by the church- and mosque-builders of the medieval Mediterranean, and were carefully disassembled for reuse or re-carved into the sarcophagi of the elite. The glazing found in many ancient Roman windows was gathered up for recycling sufficiently carefully, shard by shard, to mean that it is only recently, from the empty stone framing, that archaeologists have come to realise that it was ever there.[2] Timber, stone building blocks, roof tiles and bricks were carefully removed and redeployed – the same item often taking its place in multiple buildings over the centuries.

Perhaps the conservation of past energy investment is seen most clearly in a peculiar form of urban mining that developed. Medieval Romans knew that ancient builders had joined masonry together with lead-covered iron bars. To save the costly firewood heat of smelting new metals, these small pieces were mined from the ancient walls by energy-hungry medieval hands: recycling – today a pious duty – was then a vital source of scarce resources.

After so much was taken from the great monuments of ancient Rome, the main reason that so much remains of structures like the Baths of Caracalla is their use of unrecyclable concrete for their cores.

Even so, the craggy concrete stumps that remained after everything else had gone found use as supports and shelters for new structures, from farm buildings to churches to fortified houses. Nothing went to waste.

The contrast with today's architecture could hardly be more striking or, in the face of potential climate catastrophe, more painful. Half of all the materials now produced on Earth go into construction, and much of this goes on to become waste within a few decades.[3] Perhaps as much as half of the world's solid waste comes from the construction and demolition of buildings, and thirty-nine per cent of our greenhouse-gas emissions – the waste products that may yet wipe us out – come from the construction, operation and demolition of buildings. We may be appropriately careful to respect our leading historic monuments, but that should not disguise the fact that global modernity is incomparably the most wasteful civilisation ever to exist and our buildings are at the forefront of the environmental disaster of the waste age.

Our spectacular profligacy with materials and components would shock and disgust the world's poorest today, and even the world's richest a few centuries ago. Our current habits have emerged entirely thanks to the cheap, convenient energy provided in effectively limitless quantities by the burning of fossil fuels.[4] Inexpensive fossil-fuel energy has made materials and manufacturing far cheaper than labour, with the result that the design and craft effort involved in salvaging and reusing materials and components appears uneconomical. The cheap default option is destructive demolition, the remains trucked away swiftly by powerful diesel engines – most of it for dumping or downcycling.

At the moment, the UK construction industry is not required even to monitor the carbon emissions produced in material procurement, construction and demolition – let alone reduce them.[5] This and other aspects of waste need to be well regulated, with accurate monitoring and publication of waste figures for each project, and progressive restrictions on how much waste is permitted.

The end of each building's life needs equally to be factored in at the design stage: the two totemic materials of the waste age are concrete and plastic – each hard to adapt, and dumped or wastefully downcycled after their limited life. Concrete is currently the most used material on the planet after water, despite its high carbon footprint, its inflexibility and the fact that its end of life sees it become a low-quality material. Twenty per cent of all Europe's plastics are used in construction, much or most of it landfilled or burned when no longer useful.[6] Most pre-modern building technologies were dismantlable and reusable at the end of their life. We need to return urgently to designing for adaptation, deconstruction and reuse as integral parts of our construction technologies' lifespan.

In the UK and many other rich-world countries, relatively static population size and very extensive robust building stock ought to come together to minimise the need for new construction: as the Architects' Journal's online and social-media RetroFirst campaign argues, maintaining and upgrading our existing building stock is far more sustainable than our current cycle of demolition and replacement.[7] Yet even as it promises ever-more-ambitious sustainability goals, the current UK government has advanced pro-waste age legislation in order to incentivise the mass demolition of some of the most robust and abundant building stock in the country.[8]

Our unrealistic expectations of ordinary buildings are partly to blame for our wastefulness. A kind of comfort-conditions arms race has progressively narrowed the range of temperature that we will tolerate – producing, via massive fossil-fuel inputs for heating or cooling, interiors from the Arctic Circle to the equator in which people feel comfortable year-round in Western business clothing. Older buildings tend to be judged against absurdly narrow definitions of adequate performance (and profitability), and demolished and replaced when found wanting.

Current financial instruments, legislation and structures of insurance and liability also tend to produce powerful waste-age pressures, making it easiest and most profitable to build from scratch with all-new materials and components, for lifespans of sixty years or so. After this period, there will be no one liable if the buildings deteriorate to the point of needing replacement. There is no incentive for designing-in a right to repair: unlike almost all pre-modern buildings, our current new buildings are mostly difficult or impossible to patch up when water gets into their complex cladding systems or a glazing unit springs a leak.[9]

It doesn't need to be like this. It is encouraging to look at the scale and durability of buildings produced by societies operating before the exploitation of fossil fuels – whether in China, Persia, Mesoamerica or Zimbabwe. Even the Romans, famous for their use of concrete, managed to make theirs with vastly less wastage of fuel: today's buildings are almost entirely composed of materials that were processed using intense heat; ancient Roman buildings used heat-processed materials for less than six per cent of their volume of materials, and sourced three-quarters of them within 20 kilometres (12½ miles) of the construction site.[10]

Even now, at the height of the waste age, there are many designers working hard to establish principles and practices for a sustainable future. In this book, you can see some of the imaginative and beautiful work through which Lacaton & Vassal have brought retrofit into the spotlight, and exciting experiments with materials and techniques like 3D printing in earth that might help to reduce the wastefulness of new construction.

In their small house project in Eton, Matthew Barnett Howland and Dido Milne have explored a new material (expanded cork bark left over by the wine-bottling industry), new techniques of fabrication (laser-cutting for maximum precision, allowing them to avoid unrecyclable glues and sealants) and a new attitude to end of life (every component is held in place by gravity or screws so that all can be dismantled undamaged for best reuse or recycling) in order to achieve a building that emitted less carbon in construction than was absorbed in the growing of its materials, and that minimises waste at every stage. Other promising explorations are under way in returning to timber, straw and stone blocks – reusable and low-carbon – rather than concrete.

These important and welcome experiments are, however, condemned to remain in the minority and usually expensive for as long as they are swimming against the overwhelmingly powerful current of waste-age economics. In avoiding climate emergency, it is not the brilliance of the cutting edge but the business-as-usual of the mainstream that will determine the outcome. To bring our architecture out of the waste age, two great changes are required.

The first is well-crafted regulation, produced in the teeth of opposition from powerful lobbyists trying to protect shareholder profits at all costs. Only excellent regulation can tilt the playing field in favour of reuse, low-carbon retrofit and new architecture that escapes the waste-age norms. Designers and engineers are superb at improving technologies once adopted, and will rapidly raise the quality and lower the price of the new methods.

The second change that we need if we are to escape the waste age is a change in culture – away from the fetishisation of the shiny and new, the big and the high-performance, towards an enlightened new appreciation of what's already there. We need to love the marks of time and wear, and derive pleasure not from conspicuous consumption but from the historical particularities that produced each wrinkle of style and technique. At the moment, we retain aspects of our built environment that we define as having particular cultural value – a facade here, a sculptural roof there – but too often we demolish all but these totemic elements and build from scratch, to eke out a little more usable area or to chase ever-higher definitions of building performance.

Again, the approach of the energy-poor medieval inhabitants of Rome is inspirational. Their reuse of existing buildings was not a tokenistic cultural gesture but an essential avoidance of waste – a fundamental appreciation of the inherent material value of existing buildings. The enormous mausoleum of the Roman emperor Hadrian, for example, was reused by the papacy as a defensive structure – the Castel Sant'Angelo – and defended from attackers using cannons made with the last bronze from Hadrian's magnificent Pantheon. Its use and meaning changed, but its hundreds of thousands of tonnes of material remained in place.

If architecture continues with its current waste-age norms – a constant cycle of demolition and replacement with hard-to-repair, system-built new buildings, wasteful and lacking in character – the consensus of climate scientists suggests that we will wipe out humanity (and most other multicellular life) via decades of appalling suffering and instability. If we choose to, we can instead achieve a future in which well-designed regulations enable the brilliant creativity of our designers and engineers to produce a new, beautiful, waste-free architecture. We have the option of a future in which our architecture varies with regional materials and climate adaptations. We can re-establish traditions of local skilled crafts. Gifted designers will be needed in large numbers to make existing buildings work well via clever, low-waste interventions. We can do it – but we have to get on with it.

THE WASTE EXPLORERS

The technology we use every day, from mobile phones
to cars, has been mass manufactured using complex
materials and processes, developed and refined
over time. New products are often made of scores
of materials, so it becomes increasingly difficult
to answer the simple question: what is it made of?

Contemporary designers are uncovering information
about the materials and processes of the designed
world, inviting new dialogues about the use of
the Earth's resources. With this knowledge, we can
connect the things we consume to the raw materials
and natural resources used in their manufacture,
and in turn acknowledge the environmental and
human cost of these materials.

1 Below: The Forbo
factory calender
machine, with rollers
that flatten the
linseed oil, wood
dust and chalk
mixture into sheets
of linoleum

2 Opposite: Discarded
linoleum from Dalton
College, Alkmaar,
the Netherlands

Dutch product designer Christien Meindertsma
visits manufacturing plants and farms to investigate
how materials, processes and design can be made
environmentally sustainable. In 2019, for the
manufacturer Forbo, she researched the potential for
recycling old linoleum flooring ('lino'). Lino is a
carbon-neutral material made from linseed oil, wood
dust and chalk, backed by jute, but once discarded it
becomes rigid, dry and hard to recycle. Meindertsma
discovered that old lino could be rejuvenated simply
by feeding it through a calender machine, with
rollers to flatten and make the material flexible
and reusable once more.

1 Mosaic of different tile
techniques made from
reprocessed linoleum
from a 1990s Marmoleum
sample book, 2019.
Christien Meindertsma

1   iPhone 4S, 2018.
    Materials: Glass,
    stainless steel,
    polycarbonate, LiCo,
    graphite, PVC, PMMA,
    fibreglass, copper,
    polyethylene, PET,
    aluminium, silicon,
    silicone rubber, PVA,
    Kapton (polyimide)

tape, ceramic, magnet,
tin, PEN + PET, nickel,
foam rubber, silver,
tantalum, phosphorus,
nylon, tungsten,
gallium, cobalt,
arsenic, gold. DRIFT.
(Lonneke Gordijn and
Ralph Nauta)

2 Below: NOKIA 3210, 2018.
Materials: PC + ABS,
nylon (PA), aluminium,
PC, ABS, glass fibre,
mischmetal, glass,
nickel hydroxide, PVC,
epoxy, steel, tin,
paper, PET, photoresist
polymer, ceramic Al2O3,
adhesive, copper,
rubber, PU foam, iron,
tantalum, silicone soft,
PP, magnet, felt, brass,
germanium, gold, nickel.
DRIFT. (Lonneke Gordijn
and Ralph Nauta)

Materialism is an ongoing research project by DRIFT,
a multidisciplinary studio that takes everyday items
and investigates what materials they are made of.
By breaking down each product, from cars to pencils,
DRIFT can catalogue every component used to make these
familiar objects. The quantity of each, from greatest
to smallest, is represented as a rectangular block.
The Volkswagen Beetle, as an example, has over 40
blocks. This thorough investigation into the make-up
of everyday things re-establishes our link to their
materials and the natural world from which they
have come.

1 Opposite: Material
Recovery Facility,
Athens. Research
photograph by
Sophie Thomas for
*Rematerialise: A Library
of Possibilities*

2 Below: SWEEEP
Kuusakoski e-waste,
Kent. Research
photograph by
Sophie Thomas for
*Rematerialise: A Library
of Possibilities*

he designer and advocate for sustainable and
ircular design Sophie Thomas has gathered a
ollection of materials in different states of
ecovery. This is a resource to better understand an
xtensive range of new materials and their potential
se by designers and manufacturers. The process of
ransforming waste into a functioning material is
omplex. By both hand and machine, it is collected,
orted and washed, a process that takes both time
nd energy. Using recycled and recovered materials
educes the demand for raw materials and conserves
atural resources and the use of energy.

RECLAIMING PRECIOUS RESOURCES

Today's wealthy countries have few shortages,
but a growing and unchecked abundance of waste.
By collecting, sorting and reusing waste materials,
they can be transformed into useful, meaningful and
desirable ones. There is so much waste material in
circulation that, increasingly, there is less need
to mine the Earth for certain metals. Organised and
ethical local processing is essential to ensure
these resources are put back into circulation.

Designers are helping to evolve systems for recycling,
from small-scale community-based initiatives to high-
tech and scalable technology. By making furniture
from recycled sea plastic or regenerating old textiles
into new high-quality polymer fibres, designers are
expressing the versatility, beauty and potential of
these precious materials, meeting new demand and
securing a place in the supply chain.

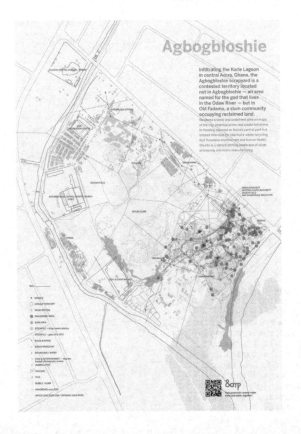

1   Opposite and below:
    Mapping of resources
    and stakeholders by
    Agbogbloshie Makerspace
    Platform, co-led by D.K.
    Osseo-Asare and Yasmine
    Abbas, 2013–present.
    Images created for the
    Seoul Biennale 2017.

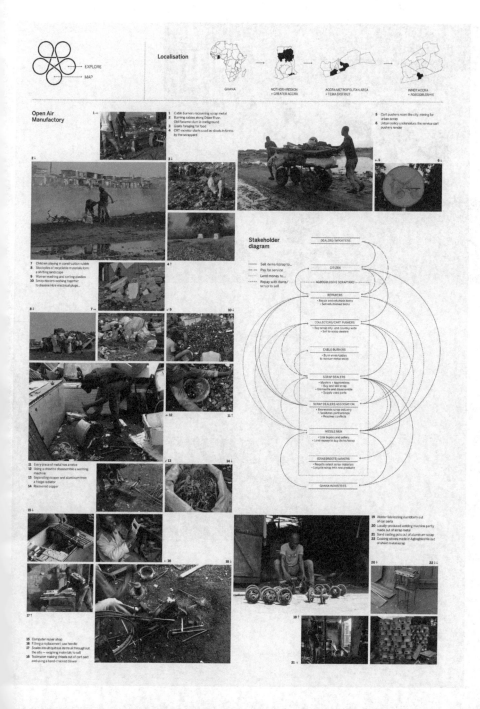

1 This spread: Stills from *Ore Streams*, 2018. Formafantasma (Simone Farresin and Andrea Trimarchi)

ormafantasma spent three years investigating the impact
f electronic and digital waste. The films from which
hese stills are taken explain their research into
he damaging environmental and human costs of current
ractice. From extracting minerals to our desire to
onsume, Formafantasma communicate the potential of
esign to initiate change and to develop more responsible
nd sustainable uses of the Earth's resources.

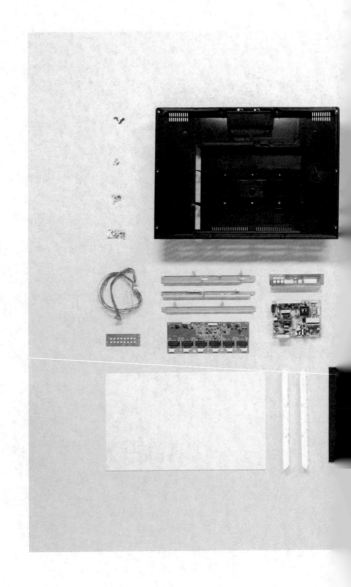

1   Still from *Ore Streams*,
     2018. Formafantasma
     (Simone Farresin and
     Andrea Trimarchi)

THE STATUS QUO BURGER

When we visit a fast-food restaurant, most of us order a beef burger, pay the bill and think nothing further of it. This simple act, when repeated more than half a million times each day in London alone, results in huge resource-use and the emission of vast quantities of greenhouse gases. Each year, London consumes just over 200 million burgers. The land needed to produce enough animal feed to produce this beef is much larger than the land area of Greater London.

At Bin Burger, we produce burger patties from organic waste, by first feeding it to animals and plants. If we were to do the same for beef, it would require a population more than three times the size of Greater London to generate the organic waste required to produce those 200 million burgers each year. Bin Burger are experimenting with new methods of turning organic waste into delicious burgers.

THE BIN BURGERS

We only make burger patties that can be produced from the organic waste collected within the Greater London area. These burgers include bean, chicken, mealworm, insect and fish. To produce 200 million Bin Burger patties requires a population much smaller than that of Greater London, and many times less than would be required to make beef burgers.

32% of Organic Waste

29% of Organic Waste

29% of Organic Waste

21% of Organic Waste

14% of Organic Waste

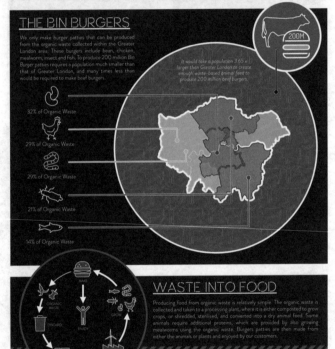

It would take a population 3.65 × larger than Greater London to create enough waste-based animal feed to produce 200 million beef burgers.

WASTE INTO FOOD

Producing food from organic waste is relatively simple. The organic waste is collected and taken to a processing plant, where it is either composted to grow crops, or shredded, sterilised, and converted into a dry animal feed. Some animals require additional proteins, which are provided by also growing mealworms using the organic waste. Burgers patties are then made from either the animals or plants and enjoyed by our customers.

1   Opposite and below:
    Bin Burger, 2021
    Concept: Greg Keeffe
    and Andy van den
    Dobbelsteen;

design: Emma Campbell,
Andy Jenkins, Sean
Cullen, Tess Blom, Nick
ten Caat, Rebecca-Jane
McConnell

This is a fictitious fast-food outlet, where London food
waste is used to fertilise or feed future food sources.
The proposal is to create a circular system of production
and waste to reduce the food industry's environmental
impact. There are lifestyle changes to be made for a
waste-free future. Are you willing to make them?.

Low-tech magazine's website is designed to minimise
the site's electricity usage and draw our attention to
waste produced by using the internet. It does this with
a range of features, including a solar-powered server,
default typefaces, smaller than average web-page sizes,
dithered or monochrome images, and offline reading
options. *Low-tech*'s open-source software has inspired
at least twenty other websites to use energy-saving
design features.

Kris De Decker, Roel Roscam Abbing, Marie Otsuka
and Lauren Traugott-Campbell, live since 2018

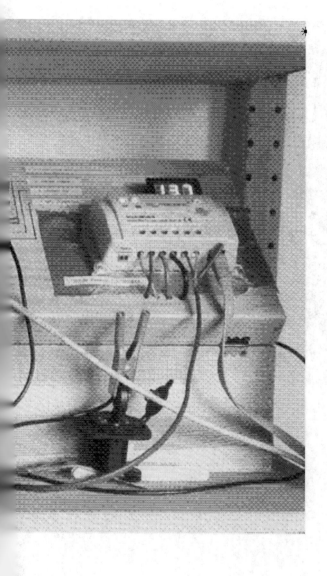

1 Opposite: The
Enviroserve e-waste
repair and recycling
facility, Rwanda

2 Below: The Recupel
e-waste recycling
facility, Belgium

E-waste is one of the fastest-growing waste streams,
and it is also one of the most valuable. Electronic
devices contain many rare metals such as gold or
titanium and large quantities of plastics and aluminium.
When e-waste is disposed of correctly, sorting and
recycling centres extract these valuable materials for
reuse. E-waste recycling generates jobs and stops toxic
chemicals and gases leaching into the environment. It
is more profitable than mining or manufacturing new
materials. For example, recycling 1 tonne of mobile
phones yields 300g of gold, while 1 tonne of extracted
gold ore, mined from the ground, yields only 3g. This
industry is growing internationally, supported by laws
such as the EU/UK Extended Producer Responsibility
Scheme in which manufacturers must cover the cost
of their products' end-of-life.

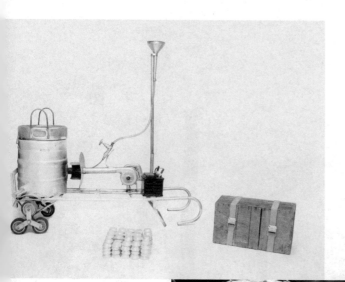

Can City is a collection of aluminium structures made from discarded drink cans collected from the streets of São Paulo. A mobile foundry, designed from salvaged materials, is used to melt the cans, using vegetable oil collected from local cafes as fuel. Moulds for the molten metal are also made from found objects. The project is inspired by Brazil's informal waste collectors, or *catadores*, who collect 80 per cent of the city's recyclable waste.

1 Opposite:
Precious Plastic,
Demonstration
of Open Source
Recycling Machines

2 Below: Chair made with
sheet plastic, produced
with bent plastic
sheets. The instructions
for this chair are
published open-source
on the Precious
Plastic website.

Precious Plastic is a grassroots movement to equip
communities to recycle plastic locally. It provides
an ever-evolving range of open-source designs to self-
build machines for recycling, including shredding,
extrusion, injection moulding and sheet-pressing.
Founder Dave Hakkens has established a website and a
wide community of recyclers to share designs, knowhow
and strategies for tackling waste plastic. From its
base in the Netherlands, Precious Plastic is connected
across the world to a growing army of people taking
action to transform plastic waste.

Dirk van der Kooij experiments with recycled plastic
from discarded household fridges to create sustainable
products. The irregular beauty of recycled plastic is
expressed in this playful 3D printed chair, made using
a self-built plastic-extruding robot that is programmed
to squeeze out layers of thick tubes of recycled
plastic to form the shape of the chair.

1   Opposite: Chubby
     Chair, 2012. Dirk
     van der Kooij

2   Below: Endless Flow
     rocking chair, 2011.
     Dirk van der Kooij

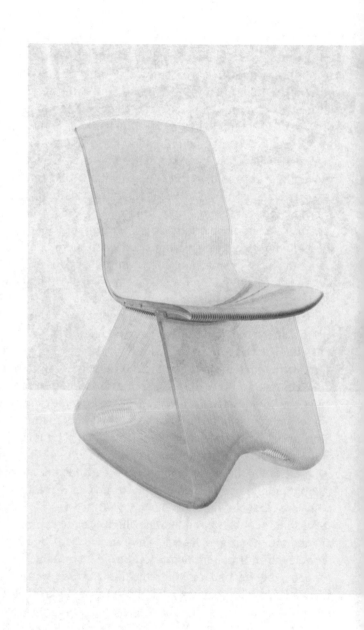

This chair has been 3D printed using recycled plastic.
A computer-controlled robotic arm extrudes a continuous
thread of molten plastic to build the chair in just over
three-and-a-half hours. Using an ex-factory printer,
designer Dirk van der Kooij adjusts the programme to
change the form and texture of the finished design.

'Purged plastic' refers to low-grade inexpensive plastic
used to clean injection-moulding machines when a colour
is changed. Taking this waste plastic from the factory
floor, Soft Baroque creates furniture that is both
sculptural and abstract, blending design and art. Their
work subverts our expectations of what the domestic
environment and the things we use should look like.

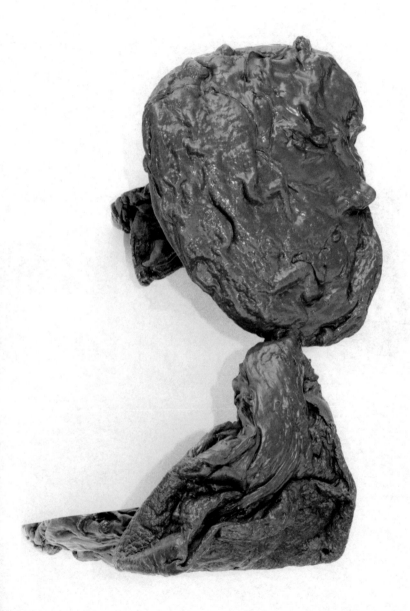

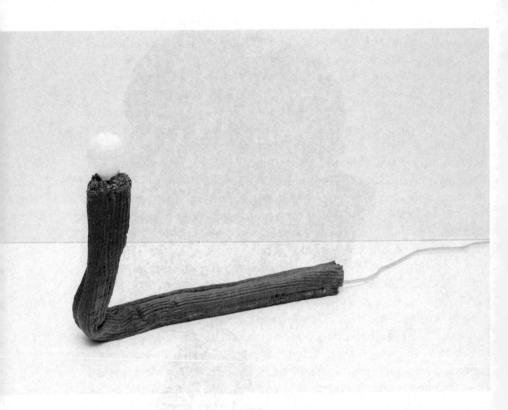

1   Opposite: Plastic
    Baroque table
    lamp, 2019.
    James Shaw

2   Below: Plastic
    Baroque armchair,
    2020. James Shaw

For his 'Plastic Baroque' furnishings, designer James
Shaw uses a self-made plastic-extruding gun to 'pipe'
confectionery-like pieces. Transforming rigid synthetic
waste into objects of value, the action of the flowing
plastic as it exits the gun is clearly expressed in the
lively forms of Shaw's furniture.

Sea Chair is made entirely from plastics recovered from
the ocean. Collaborating with fishermen, Studio SWINE
collected plastic at sea, separating it into colours and
types before shredding and melting, using seawater to
cool and set the plastic. By documenting the quantity of
plastic fishermen 'catch' in a single trip, the project
highlights the amount of plastic in our oceans.

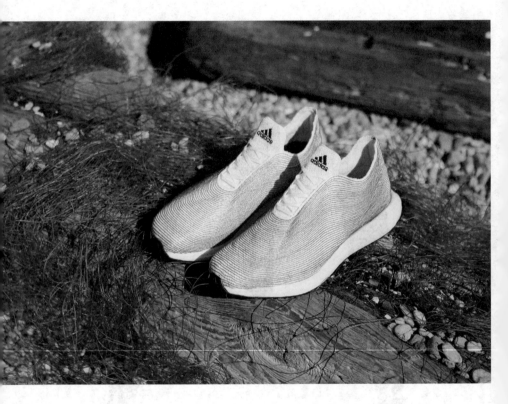

1 This spread: adidas
× Parley for the Ocean
trainer, 2016. Design:
adidas and Alexander
Taylor; manufacture:
adidas × Parley for
the Oceans

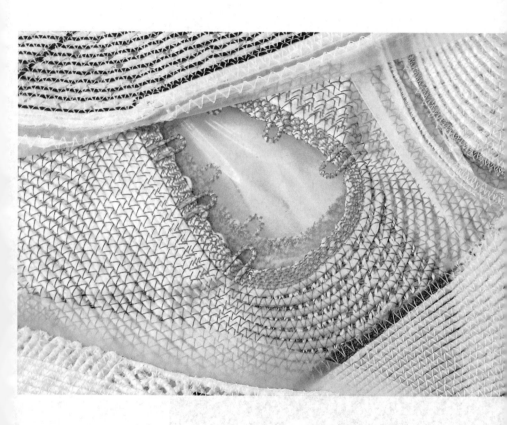

These trainers use only recycled plastic. The upper
is made from rescued deep-sea gill nets, the rest
from plastic washed up on the coastline of the
Maldives. The Maldives' government had commissioned
environmental group Parley for the Oceans to help
manage the problem of marine plastics pollution.
Since 2017, more than 25 million recycled trainers
and other garments have been produced.

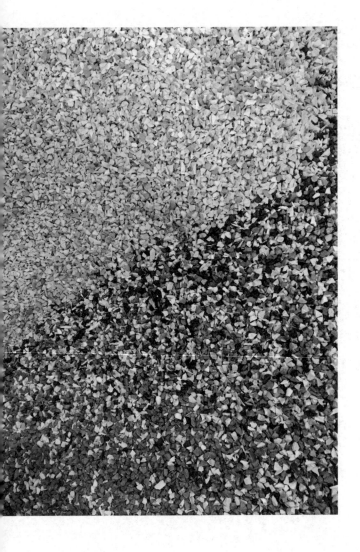

Architecture practice Snøhetta converted plastic waste
from Norwegian fishing companies into new furniture.
Connecting this waste stream to a nearby manufacturer
increases the incentive to gather and recycle rather
than abandon used fishing equipment. The surface
pattern captures the flow of the liquid plastic and
evokes the swirl of the breaking waves, making a visual
connection to recycled fishing nets and ropes.

KNOT uses human hair as a natural and sustainable
alternative to the polyester widely used to make rope
for the fishing industry. About 6.5 million kilograms
of hair is discarded by UK hairdressers every year,
while about 640,000 tonnes of fishing rope is jettisoned
into the sea. Exploiting hair's natural properties of
tensile strength, oil absorbency and thermal insulation,
designer Sanne Visser uses her open-source, semi-
automated rope-making machine to produce plastic-free
ropes, addressing two waste problems at once.

1 This spread:
Ropes from KNOT,
2019 Studio
Sanne Visser

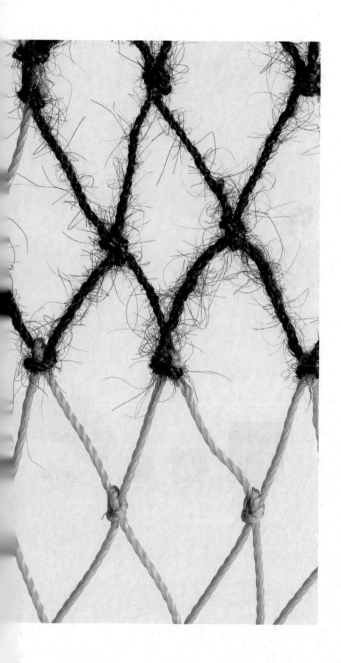

1 This spread: The Tyre
Collective (Siobhan
Anderson, Hanson Cheng,
Deepak Mallya and Hugo
Richardson), 2020

ngineers and scientists at the Tyre Collective are
eveloping a device, to be attached to car wheels, that
ill capture tyre wear, a microplastic pollutant. Tyre
articles are released into the air every time a vehicle
rakes or turns, affecting our lungs and settling into
ur waterways. The Tyre Collective converts particles
f tyre wear into useful products, such as shoe soles,
layground surfaces and rubber bricks.

1   This spread: Range of
    surface materials made
    from ceramic and glass
    waste, 2015–ongoing.
    Alusid (co-founded by
    David Stuart Binns and
    Alasdair Bremmer)

Alusid is the result of a research project at the
University of Central Lancashire which sought to
explore how low-value materials such as old ceramic
toilets or post-consumer glass could be diverted
from landfill and transformed into quality surface
materials. Their tiles and sheet materials are
manufactured from at least 98 per cent waste material
and they are currently developing recycled glazes
and scaling up their production while addressing the
logistical challenges of ensuring reliable supply
chains of waste material.

1   Construction materials
    being salvaged from
    Belgacom/Rue Lebeau,
    Brussels, before
    demolition by Rotor
    Deconstruction

Rotor is a design and architecture cooperative that
challenges how architects and builders think about
construction waste. In 2016, they set up an architectural
salvage company to reclaim and reuse construction and
interior materials. Although new buildings are usually
more energy efficient, the demolition of older structures
is causing an increase in global construction waste,
which is estimated to double to 2.2 billion tonnes a year
by 2025. This office block in the centre of Brussels,
formerly owned by state telecom company Belgacom, is
scheduled for total demolition. Among the waste materials
salvaged by Rotor were marble slabs, ceramic sinks and
tiles, and stainless-steel rails and door handles.

1 Opposite: Construction materials being salvaged from Belgacom/ Rue Lebeau, Brussels, before demolition by Rotor Deconstruction

2 Below: K-Briq, 2020–ongoing Design: Kenoteq (Gabriela Medero and Samuel Chapman); manufacture: Kenoteq Ltd

The K-Briq is a sustainable building brick made from at least 90 per cent recycled construction and demolition waste. Around 2.6 billion bricks are used in UK construction every year, many having been imported from Europe. The K-Briq uses local waste materials and is produced without using fossil fuels for firing, releasing only a tenth of the carbon emissions of a traditional fired-clay brick.

Numerous construction materials are demolished, and they are going to be sent to the landfills or crashed.

If you're careful, basically everything is (re)usable in one shape or form.

1 Opposite: Village demolition and reclamation in China. Qin Nan Meng, 2021

2 Opposite: A rural reclamation yard in the UK. Ele How Yun Man, 2021

3 Below: The destruction and salvage of tiles in Florianópolis, Brazil. Amaya Hernandez, 2021

4 Below: A souk for second-hand building materials in Casablanca, Morocco. Jihane-may Slaoui, 2021

We even have tiles from a hundred years ago

At night when we pack everything, the market is invaded by the residents, and their kids play here.

During lockdowns prompted by the Covid-19 pandemic, students at the Architectural Association were asked to investigate the ecosystems of building material reuse in their local area. The short films they produced – stills of which are shown here – give a glimpse of various reuse practices, ancient and modern, across four continents.

The fashion designer Bethany Williams creates her
collections using deadstock and other forms of fashion
waste. The spring/summer 2021 collection by Bethany
Williams celebrates and supports the Magpie Project,
a Newham-based initiative that works with children and
mothers who are homeless or at risk of homelessness.
The collection uses waste materials such as deadstock/
second-hand tracksuits and book publishing waste covers
as well as non-toxic inks and organic, hand-woven
wool fabrics.

A pioneer of sustainable high-end fashion, Stella
McCartney has consistently developed and championed
ways to reduce the environmental impact of her
designs. Her approaches include developing plant-based
alternatives to animal-derived materials, using waste or
deadstock in her collections, and supporting innovative
material technology to replace virgin cellulose or
synthetic materials. She recently published a manifesto
that outlines her brand's ethos and pledges future
action. Entitled *A to Z*, it starts with 'Accountable'
and ends with 'Zero Waste'.

1   Opposite: ECONYL®
     jacket and trousers,
     2019. Design: Stella
     McCartney; materials:
     ECONYL®, made by
     Aquafil, Italy

2   Below: Z for Zero Waste
     dress, 2021. Made from
     repurposed excess
     printed stock from
     nine previous Stella
     McCartney collections.
     Design: Stella McCartney

This fur-free fur is made from a new soft fibre called
Sorona®. Created from 37 per cent plant-based materials
with recycled polyester, it can be recycled back into
PET at the end of its life. The trousers are made
from 100 per cent recycled polyester from plastic
bottle waste.

1   Opposite: KOBA® coat   2   Below: Infinite hoodie,
     and trousers, 2021.   2019. Design: Stella
     Design: Stella McCartney   McCartney

Chemical recycling technologies are used to create
new fabrics, such as NuCycl™, from discarded clothing.
The fabric can be broken down and regenerated multiple
times without loss of quality.

1 Below: Quilted Puff
   Jacket Jkt 402 and
   Quilted Puff Skirt
   Skt 403, 2020. Design:
   Phoebe English.
   Reclaimed silk wool
   sourced from studios
   and factories in London,
   and stuffed with organza
   silk offcuts produced
   from making the garment
   to the right.

2   Below: Fragment Dress
    Txt Drs 358, 2019.
    Design: Phoebe English.
    Outer: silk organza;
    inner: offcuts of
    Okeo-tex100 certified
    bamboo viscose left
    over from the previous
    season's studio production 'waste'
    and incorporated into
    the new season's work;
    worn over Apron Slip
    Dress Drs 346: Okeo-tex
    100 certified bamboo
    viscose made using a
    zero-waste pattern-
    cutting technique.

Currently, the UK offers little to no textile recycling
facilities or incentives to reuse pre-consumer textile
waste. Phoebe English developed her 'fragment textile'
and quilting technique to use offcuts from her own
studio's textile waste in new work. Experimenting with
quilting techniques and zero-waste pattern-cutting,
English captures scraps of fabric between layers of
outer materials with various textiles techniques to
create new clothes.

1   Opposite: East Tilbury
Landfill. Images by
Isabel Fletcher on
research trip.

2   Below: Detail of Offcut
Textile Drape, 2021
Isabel Fletcher

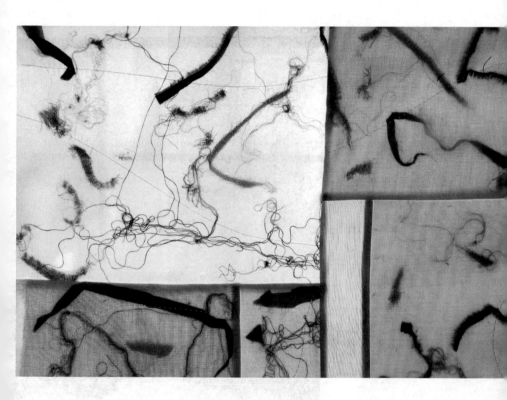

Made from 100 per cent waste offcuts, scraps and
threads, this textile hanging was inspired by
East Tilbury Landfill in Essex, a household waste
site from 1930 to 1980. Today, waste from the site
is being unearthed and swept into the Thames due
to coastal erosion. The work conveys the often-
unappreciated beauty of waste and the need to
care for the things we discard.

1   Below: Bale of
discarded jeans.
Renewcell

2   Bottom: Extracting
cellulose through a
textile pulping process.
Renewcell

3   Below: Sheets of
    Circulose, ready
    to be shipped to
    manufacturers who
    will spin this sheet
    into thread to makenew
    garments. Renewcell

4   Bottom: Levi's jeans
    manufactured with
    Circulose. Renewcell

orldwide, 25 million tonnes of cotton and viscose go
o landfill every year. Textile recycling generates
ew jobs and reduces the need to grow cotton – a
and-, water- and energy-intensive process. Since
012, the Swedish manufacturer Renewcell has
eveloped Circulose, a new material made from cotton
ecovered from worn-out clothes, creating a circular
roduction loop for textiles.

1 This spread: A textile
   woven from industrial
   plastic manufacturing
   waste, 2021. Design:
   Shubhi Sachan;
   manufacture: Material
   Library of India

This woven material is made from non-recyclable,
multi-layered, foil-backed plastics, which are produced
in abundance across the globe. Applying traditional
handweaving and craft techniques to this waste material,
it is converted into a high-value textile. The intention
is to reduce disposal and minimise the use of raw
materials. This fabric is part of a larger project
called the Material Library of India, which aims to
educate people about diverting waste through design.

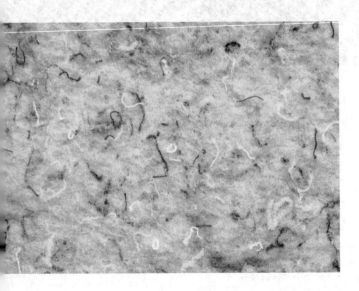

1   This spread: BAUX
acoustic felt, 2021.
Design: Form Us With
Love; manufacture: BAUX

These sound-absorbing panels are made from 100
per cent waste from the Swedish textile industry.
They are designed to produce no offcuts or excess
materials, being pressed into a single standardised
sheet that can be cut into smaller sizes. They can
also be recycled at their end of life and can be
mounted on supporting stands to divide a space.

REUSE – VALUING WHAT WE HAVE

By investing time and skill, our attitude to the
things we throw away or no longer want can be
reframed. To prevent waste, designers and architects
are creating work that values the discarded by
reusing, repairing or adapting what we already
have. The desire for the new or different is hard-
wired but, by making things more relevant to our
needs and aspirations, designers can greatly
reduce our carbon emissions.

The arguments against repair – that something
does not warrant the investment of time and skill
– ignore the embodied carbon held in our 'stuff'.
This is the amount of greenhouse gas released
during the extraction, production and processing
of materials and products. A new-build house in
the UK releases the equivalent of around 45 tonnes
of carbon dioxide in its construction, the same
that would be released if you drive around the
Earth ten times.

Textile artist and mender Celia Pym practises visible
repairing, a process that draws attention to the wear
and tear sustained by our clothes. This exposes the
past life of the piece and the person who wore it.
During the COVID-19 lockdown, Pym turned from repairing
clothes to repairing the paper bags from her daily
grocery shopping. Careful darning gives each bag a new
and different life. At a time of fear and uncertainty,
the project gave hope that something torn and worthless
could again be cherished and become significant.

1   Croft Lodge Studio,
2016. Kate Darby
Architects and David
Connor Design

This architectural project questions the
emotional and environmental cost of demolishing
and building new, which means that resources
and history are lost, rather than reusing or
remodelling old buildings. The designers built
a modern design studio with guest accommodation
around a dilapidated 300-year-old ruin, preserving
its structure and original contents, including
dust, dead bats and small sculptures. The ruin
would otherwise have been demolished and burnt,
creating unnecessary carbon emissions.

1 Opposite:
530 Dwellings, Bordeaux,
2017. Exterior before
Lacaton & Vassal's
construction

2 Below:
Transformation of
530 Dwellings,
Bordeaux, 2017. Anne
Lacaton and Jean-
Philippe Vassal with
Frédéric Druot and
Christophe Hutin

Pritzker Prize-winning architects Anne Lacaton
and Jean-Philippe Vassal see architecture as a
tool to improve the quality of life for individuals
and communities, but without negatively impacting
the environment. They use materials sparingly and
relish the restrictions of a modest budget. When
transforming three blocks of social housing in
Bordeaux, Lacaton & Vassal added generous light-
filled balconies and winter gardens that respond
to the needs of the occupants while respecting
the integrity of the original architecture.

1   This spread: Sugru
    mouldable glue,
    2003. Designer: Jane
    Ni Dhulchaointigh;
    manufacture: tesa SE

Sugru is a mouldable glue for fixing everyday objects.
t is strong, flexible, electrically insulating,
emperature-resistant, food-safe and durable. Although
t is made from plastic, it makes a positive impact by
xtending an object's lifespan. This is reminiscent of
he Japanese kintsugi tradition of visible repairs,
hich adds value to objects that were broken. Sugru aims
o make repair intuitive and easy, converting a broken
tem into something attractive and desirable.

INDICE DE RÉPARABILITÉ

INDICE DE RÉPARABILITÉ

INDICE DE RÉPARABILITÉ

INDICE DE RÉPARABILITÉ

INDICE DE RÉPARABILITÉ

Above:
France is the first country in Europe to implement
a Repairability Index. Since January 2021, French law
has required clear information on the repairability of
five categories of electronics: smartphones, laptops,
washing machines, televisions and lawnmowers. The score
is self-graded by manufacturers, using a spreadsheet
provided by the Ministry of Environment. It aims to help
consumers choose repairable products and thus motivate
manufacturers to improve repairability. More product
categories and criteria will be added by 2024.

Opposite:
iFixit is a global online community where people teach
each other to fix broken electronics and electrical
gadgets. The website publishes instructions and repair
manuals, assigning difficulty scores to projects. It
sells spares and tools that give access to products
that have been designed to keep users out, such as
a screwdriver for an iPhone 4. iFixit has also been
lobbying governments for repairability legislation
since 2003, with some success.

REPAIR MANIFESTO

WE HOLD THESE TRUTHS TO BE SELF-EVIDENT

IF YOU CAN'T FIX IT, YOU DON'T OWN IT.

REPAIR IS BETTER THAN RECYCLING
Making our things last longer is both more efficient and more cost-effective than mining them for raw materials.

REPAIR SAVES YOU MONEY
Fixing things is often free, and usually cheaper than replacing them. Doing the repair yourself saves you money.

REPAIR TEACHES ENGINEERING
The best way to find out how something works is to take it apart.

REPAIR SAVES THE PLANET
Earth has limited resources. Eventually we will run out. The best way to be efficient is to reuse what we already have.

REPAIR CONNECTS PEOPLE AND THINGS | **REPAIR IS WAR ON ENTROPY** | **REPAIR IS SUSTAINABLE**

WE HAVE THE RIGHT:

TO DEVICES THAT CAN BE OPENED

TO REPAIR DOCUMENTATION FOR **EVERYTHING**

TO REPAIR THINGS IN THE PRIVACY OF OUR OWN HOMES | TO ERROR CODES & WIRING DIAGRAMS

TO CHOOSE OUR OWN REPAIR TECHNICIAN | TO NON-PROPRIETARY **FASTENERS**

TO REMOVE 'DO NOT REMOVE' STICKERS

TO REPLACE **ANY & ALL** CONSUMABLES OURSELVES | TO TROUBLESHOOTING INSTRUCTIONS & FLOWCHARTS

TO AVAILABLE, REASONABLY-PRICED SERVICE PARTS

REPAIR IS INDEPENDENCE SAVES MONEY & RESOURCES | REQUIRES CREATIVITY | MAKES CONSUMERS INTO CONTRIBUTORS | INSPIRES PRIDE IN OWNERSHIP

1 Opposite: Rosie the
Restarter #1 — a
women's restart party
at the Makerversity,
London, 2014

2 Below: A repair café in
Houten, the Netherlands.
Part of a global network
of 2,178 repair cafés,
started by Martine
Postma in 2007

Across the world, thousands of repair cafés and repair
parties help people to fix their broken items, from
vacuum cleaners and cameras to socks and coffee machines.
These groups strongly believe in the right to repair as
an environmental priority. They lobby governments through
protests, petitions and education programmes, holding
companies accountable for ensuring their products are
repairable at an affordable price, with instructions
and spare parts. Repairing minimises waste, fosters
friendships, creates jobs and builds new relationships
between us and the objects we own, while also reducing
carbon emissions and the need for raw materials.

03 POST WASTE

ARE WE PREPARED FOR
A BIOTECH REVOLUTION?
**Natsai Audrey Chieza in conversation
with Justin McGuirk**

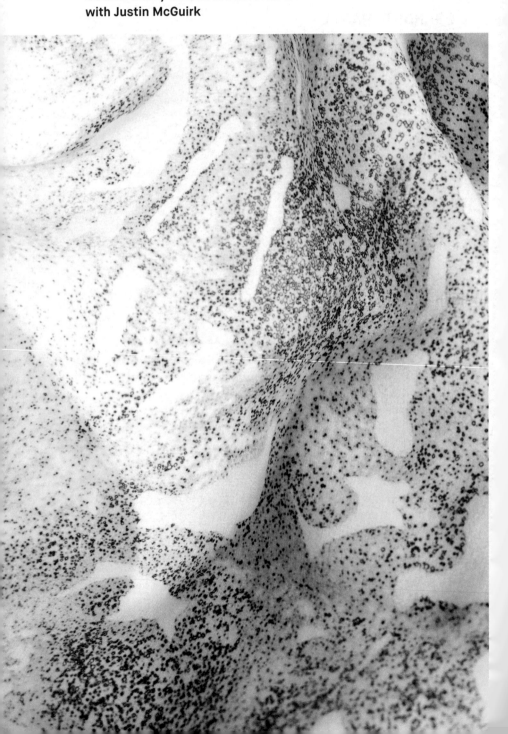

1   Opposite: in collaboration
    Project Coelicolor,   with Professor John
    detail of textile   Ward, Department
    dyed with microbial   of Biochemical
    pigments, 2013-19   Engineering, UCL
    Design: Natsai Audrey
    Chieza, Faber Futures,

JM   I wonder if we could start with you defining biodesign and saying how you feel about the term?

NAC   In very direct terms, biodesign is a field that has emerged in the context of synthetic biology, a technoscientific discipline that seeks to customise living systems so that they can have new functionality. So, where we used to brew yeast to get beer, the question became: can we engineer yeast to make products other than alcohol? And the answer to that question is yes, you can. Designers have been exploring these possibilities, sometimes incorporating genetic engineering, other times working with living systems that have certain performative qualities, such as growing mycelium for leather-like materials. And so, given the planetary-scale ecological and climate crises we face, at least from my perspective, we need to ask ourselves what we can use this ecosystem of awesomely powerful technology for. And I use the word 'awesome' carefully. I don't mean, 'awesome, that's great', but awesome as in, it's so great that we have to take it quite seriously. And that matters because we are talking about investing billions of dollars in these new infrastructures to effectively ferment and produce new biological systems, either within natural environments or outside them.
          As a designer trained in architecture and textiles, I understood the notion that there were organism designers who engineer living systems as an invitation for the design industry to contend with. What is being designed by scientists and genetic engineers at the molecular scale has real-world impacts, most of which we cannot yet quantify. And so the macro perspective, for me, is where design can really think hard about what products we create and the context in which we do this. But also, more broadly, what systems and infrastructures do we need to design to be able to incorporate these technologies? Because if we are not careful, there is a risk that we create more of the same systems that have fuelled consumption and global inequities. So biodesign is a helpful term to describe the coming together of fields of understanding, but it doesn't go far enough to reveal the complexities of what needs to be designed for its utility to provide shared benefits.

JM   Could you give us an example of how Faber Futures uses biodesign or synthetic biology to reduce waste?

NAC   Project Coelicolor looks to replace harmful chemicals in the textile dye industry with natural dyes that are derived from bacteria that naturally produce pigment molecules. Beyond offering a drop-in replacement dye, our interest also lies in how we can incorporate some kind of design logic to the protocols, or methods of fermentation, to print and dye textiles in a way that celebrates the organism's variables. We have spent a lot of time developing ways of generating prints, patterns and textures through using custom fermentation tools and methods. There's a deep sense of craft in collaboration with the organism where we provide the conditions for growth, and the organism essentially does its thing. The resultant textiles are emotive and connect the wearer to the process, something we hope reinforces the kind of provenance that enables consumers to take care of their garment, wear them for longer, and appreciate their value.

JM   Biodesign, and projects like Coelicolor, are happening at the laboratory scale but, for them to have the kinds of impact we need, do they need to be scaled up to something comparable to industrial scale, even though they're not 'industrial' per se? I wonder if there's a contradiction in trying to 'industrialise' them.

NAC   Well, yes, it's a contradiction, but it depends on which way you want to look at it. I think it's a contradiction if we don't contend with the system itself to determine how we can replace the harmful biomolecule with one that is natural and does no harm and is non-toxic. And then what we have to ask ourselves is: where are we taking that input? Are we taking it to fast fashion, for example? Because if we do that, then what we are essentially doing is divesting from fossil fuel chemicals to use the kinds of inputs that are required for natural fermentation, like sugar, to make them work on a scale of an industry that was reliant on fossil fuels. And the mathematics doesn't make sense there because of the amount of land-use required – all of that carbon input, all of that sugar! So this becomes a land management question. Scaling up is something that we also need to think of in a *smaller* way, in a more distributed way, as opposed to something centralised. And what I mean by that is that with biology we have an abundance of materiality, of biomass, that can manage scaling up. The Amazon rainforest is a great example of how biology can scale. The question is: what is it scaling to service and for what kind of demand? I think, so far, we have had this mindset that there's endless growth, and that there are no planetary boundaries. Part of the work that now needs to be done is to bring in a new consensus about consumption and what that looks like. And the notion of throwaway culture, of fast fashion, for example, is completely incompatible with biological fabrication, as far as I'm concerned, because then we're not making real change, it's just greenwashing. It's very difficult to contend with the recent IPCC report on climate change and think that the solution to solving these problems is to find another way for the fashion industry's demand-generating business model to hold. So our scaling efforts really have to be tied to a new social consensus.

JM   I think this is a critical point. There are new technologies and there are new dyeing processes and new forms of fabrication emerging, but what you are saying is that these technologies need to be distributed rather than centralised. And that we need to change the whole consumerist model. Now, that is a complex social issue. But in terms of distributed manufacturing, this is interesting, because it is analogous to, say, the promise that 3D printing would obviate everything being made in one place and shipped across the world. How does that play out in your imagination when it comes to processes like dyeing?

NAC   I think we have precedents already across the world. There are communities who still have time-honoured textile fabrication processes, including dyeing and weaving. Artisanal production is something that we like to fetishise but it is actually very much rooted in community-based making, sharing resources, etc. And I think part of the problem in the more richly resourced nations of the world is that everything has become so fast that we are dislocated from our supply chains. The social aspect of knowing where your garments come from no longer exists exist except for the privileged few. In actual fact, we have the complete opposite, which is – to use the 'one-click' purchase option of online retail giants like

Amazon as an example – that we are encouraged to be thoughtless and impulsive about how we consume every single thing around us. And it is sold to us as a mark of success that we can consume with no boundaries.

Where I am most fascinated by distributed modes of production and consumption is in the global south, where so much of it is not driven by any kind of ethos or sustainability credentials, but out of scarcity and resilience. So people are resourceful and come together as a community to build things, deconstruct things and rebuild things. A great analogy for that is the e-waste subcultures that exist, where there are hackathons happening in the middle of a landfill, and the emergence of that is very particular to its context. I'm not saying that we should be staging hackathons in landfills in the UK (nor am I glorifying the landfill, of course), but we have to deal with why it is that we have absolutely no concept of how things are made and unmade. And I think it is because we live within a system that actively encourages us to be ignorant. So the question is, what does it look like to build an alternative system, where people are very deliberate about how things are being made? Biology offers a unique starting point to reset the conversation around how we consume things by bringing forward the lens of nature and technology. Fundamentally it's about the relationship we wish to have with nature.

JM   That's a fascinating picture that you are conjuring of a local but biological production.

NAC   The local aspects are really important because if you take the logic of capitalism – which is: I own something, it's my intellectual property, nobody else can have it – that means we are not going to have as much innovation as we would like to see. Instead, if we had more people working on this, we would be further along the road. What I am very weary of is when the biggest players start to put a block on who can participate in this landscape. It will be very sad if all of this experimentation boils down to a question of 'who owns nature?' And that's a very important point because we are currently losing so much of nature to climate catastrophe and the solutions that are being proposed are bundled up in IP protections.

JM   I suppose, then, that it is about moving to a 'designing with' model, where the living material is an active agent in the process and not just a static material to be shaped or formed. If I take a step back, design and industrialisation presuppose a great deal of control and stability, as well as predictability and permanence. The whole point of industrialisation is that you can standardise and maintain that standardisation. So I'm wondering whether, when you're designing with biological materials and processes, that opens the door to a new kind of aesthetics where it is less about standardisation and more about the unpredictable, the uncontrollable, the impermanent?

NAC   This has been, I think, the one piece that has kept me interested in this field since I started in 2011. My first experiments with *Streptomyces Coelicolor* (pigment-producing bacteria) were based on an approach that followed this logic: ferment the organism, extract the pigment, plug and play into your normal textile dyeing process or screen-printing process. So I tried and I failed, and I failed for about a year before, in a last throw of the dice, I started to grow the organism directly onto the textile. That's when this entire world of variability emerged. And the aesthetics were difficult to come to terms with because they were not what I had in mind for what I was trying to accomplish. I had to build myriad different tools to mediate, if you like, the growth conditions of this organism so that it would effect the aesthetic vision I was trying to build.

JM   And that suggests a world in which the designer is not the visionary, who achieves exactly what she has in mind, but is in fact the steward of an unpredictable process?

NAC   Yes. It's a very humbling thing to work with nature. And to work with nature as a non-scientist is also very difficult because you are often asking the same questions, but your solution to them is fundamentally different to how a scientist might approach it. So, for me, the question has always been, how do you get everyone in the room understanding each other's language and oriented around the same goal despite differences in processing knowledge? That's when you can start to see real opportunities emerging that go beyond

yourself and move firmly into a collaborative space. And there's no
'starchitect' here. It is just not possible.

JM   You mentioned earlier your slight scepticism about these
nascent technologies, that these materials are in a very early stage
of exploration, so one needs to be careful not to raise expectations of
them too high. Could you say more about that?

NAC   It is hard because I think the critique is valid. But we have
also come a long way. In the last decade, we have seen work go from
laboratory enquiry into full-blown start-up. We have seen brands like
Hermès, a luxury fashion label, really embrace the potential of new
mycelium-based materials for luxury goods. That is huge. We are
entering a stage where we have that kind of buy-in and investment
starting to back the efforts that people have been building for a
decade. In terms of getting people's hopes up, I think it is difficult
because demand for solutions and alternatives is growing rapidly.
But if we could be more cognisant of how tech development pans out,
to see materials coming on board now is quite incredible. I think in the
next two to five years, we are going to see more consumer products
available on the market. My issue, however, is whether consumers
and the business supply chains are ready for that, whether they are
prepared for a biotech revolution.
            My first TED talk was 'Fashion has a pollution problem
– can biology fix it?', and my answer to that has always been 'no'.
But it is a tool, and if a tool is layered with other interventions then
we have a better chance at improving these pretty toxic systems.
So it is about being upfront with people and not saying 'This is a
panacea that can fix everything.' Instead, this is a solution to a
specific set of problems.

WORKING SYMBIOTICALLY
WITH NATURAL SYSTEMS
Julia Watson in conversation
with Justin McGuirk

JM   Perhaps you could start by telling us about how ancient, indigenous forms of technology can steer designers towards more effective ways of tackling the environmental crisis?

JW   I think there's a position that's been taken in design that is very Western- or Euro-American-centric, and that has taken over the environmental and climate-change conversation, marginalising a lot of really relevant voices that can speak to thousands of years' worth of knowledge. For an industry such as landscape architecture, which appears to be innovative in terms of green technology, there's a great depth of understanding about how to exist with natural systems that is just being completely ignored. And there are many reasons why that has happened, but the ones you can point to are colonialism, racism and imperialism. And so, I think it's important to open up that conversation, and to understand that there are many ways in which people can live with nature. And these contextualise cultural understandings of how humans and environments can relate to one another in different ways. That's why I think we need a new mythology of technology that is derived from thousands of years of thinking, rather than 300 years of thinking.

JM   The 300 years you refer to take us back to the Enlightenment, and you are obviously challenging an Enlightenment worldview as well as the project of modernity and the modernist movement specifically. So, you're challenging a lot that the architecture and design world still holds dear.

JW   Part of what I think has been happening is that there's been almost a neocolonialism of the design industry where, in the climate-change context, people are taking solutions around the world and applying them universally. We see that in places like Jakarta or in India, and that is part of colonialism. We may have a universal 1.5-degree temperature rise but the catastrophic impacts of climate change happen at a local scale. What's so incredible about these technologies is that they are place-based technologies that have evolved at a local scale, based on climate extremes and climate adaptation to those extremes over a long time. The Dutch, for instance, will come and sell you their polder technology, whereas a polder technology already exists in China, and in Jakarta. There's a polder technology that exists in India that deals with salt water and fresh water, that is agricultural and that is locally based, born of monsoon conditions and catering to that local ecosystem. As designers, how can we use these technologies rather than erasing them – so that we're keeping cultural-heritage and environmental resources, living within the scarcity of local conditions, involving the local community? Hyper-local solutions are likely to be more socially and environmentally equitable than our universal solutions.

JM   Well, there's the colonialism problem and then there's the Enlightenment problem and the idea of 'man mastering nature'. What I take from your book, *Lo-TEK*, is that designers have become too removed from nature – which is abundantly clear – and that these Indigenous communities have an inherent eco-intelligence that we lack.

JW   They *are* nature. They don't think of themselves as being *separate* to nature.

JM   So, it's a philosophical problem.

JW   Partly, yes. And that's why I talk about a cultural understanding being needed. We have a superiority complex but we also have a saviour complex: now, we're going to 'save' nature. What I postulate in the book is that these technologies work symbiotically with natural systems. There is an understanding from the material – from a single reed, say – to a straw building all the way to the systems and the infrastructural scale: simply working symbiotically with natural systems and taking advantage of water-cleansing abilities, construction abilities – even the decomposition of the internal tissue of a particular plant species, which creates buoyancy. Decomposition is actually an advantageous performative quality if you want to create floating islands.

JM   Can you tell us more about that example?

JW   The Uros community – who live in Peru, on Lake
Titicaca, which I talk about in the book – create brick modules
out of the root base of the totora reed, which is the prevalent reed
surrounding that lake. They use that particular reed to create these
brick modules out of which they build the islands, the houses,
the boats – and they also eat it. There are three different types of
decomposition occurring in the structure of these brick modules,
and they take advantage of the buoyancy that offers to create these
floating islands that last for twenty-five years. Or there's the Ma'dan
people who live in the southern wetlands of Iraq, who create the
al-tahla islands out of a different reed. They use a similar technique
to the one used by the Sumerians a thousand years ago, where they
use the reed to make columns and rafters; they weave it into walls,
floors and roofs; and then they twist it to create a twine that then
wraps around the building to hold it together. And the buildings can
be deconstructed and moved in three days. It's a really innovative
and versatile system that understands how to get as much as
you can performatively out of one a single material that's
completely biodegradable.

JM   Given that example of how rotting can be the crucial
performative quality, I've been thinking that perhaps we need to
start to see decomposition as an asset. This would be completely
antithetical to everything that design espouses. Of course, we talk
a lot about designed obsolescence but not literal rotting. We – the
design industry – need to get more comfortable with decomposition
and with the aesthetics of imperfection.

JW   With organic processes, yes. If your material palette
is glass and steel, you're not working with living material. And it
becomes a very different thing when you start working with living
material that's decomposing and going into a different stage.

JM   I'd like to talk about the East Kolkata wetlands, an
example that you document in the book, because it's specifically
about waste in the most literal sense. It's not quite ancient – it's
from the early twentieth century – but it is certainly indigenous
and natural.

JW   It's a large-scale agricultural system of 350 fish ponds that are owned by a collective of farmers. It takes in half the sewage daily from the city of Kolkata, which is home to 15 million people. So, it's taking 700 million tonnes of raw sewage and processing it into clean water that can then travel into the Bay of Bengal. And that process takes forty days. It all began, apparently, when a farmer accidentally let sewage water into his fish farm. He expected that it would kill his fish but in fact it increased his yield, and so other farmers began to adopt it. So, there's an adaptation from place-based observation occurring. The water comes in through a series of canals and then goes into settling ponds, just like any wastewater treatment or artificial wetland system. After a period of time in the settling ponds, when you see the water change colour, it is released into agriculture ponds. And the agriculture ponds are obviously conditioned based upon the age of different types of fish. And they rotate water through those ponds, and then it's released. But the system is really interesting in that it is both cleaning the water and providing food for the city. The fish is sold in Kolkata, and the clean water is irrigating rice and vegetable farms that lie around this system. It's reducing the costs of having to have trucks go out into the countryside and bring vegetables and rice back. It's reducing the cost of having to buy irrigation water. It's pretty incredible biodiversity. It's also carbon sequestering, and it's a beautiful landscape. So, it provides all these incredible services, and saves the city about $21 million worth in annual operating costs for a sewage-treatment plant. So, this is a free service, and these fishermen don't get any remuneration. In fact, they're threatened by development because the fringes of this area are constantly being developed for new 'eco cities'.

JM   It's an incredible case study. But, rather than working with waste, is there an example from your research of how we can simply create *less waste*?

JW   I'm really interested in the idea of industrial symbiosis. In places like Kalundborg, in Denmark, industries are setting up multi-stakeholder partnerships to reduce waste or to identify input and output streams. That can be used by different industries collaborating so that you're really not getting any waste coming out of the system, because someone's output becomes another person's input. For example, should a bakery and a brewery be located next to each other so that they can share the inputs and outputs of a fermentation process? There are about eight different examples of this type of industrial symbiosis in Scandinavia. How do we design industrial processes and industrial areas to make use of those outputs at an urban scale?

JM   Coming back to an earlier point about challenging the modernist project, have you encountered resistance from those who may see in your project a nostalgia for the 'primitive'? It should be clear that the book is not always literal, it's more metaphorical, but ...

JW   Exactly; it's a parable. But, yes, there's been some resistance from people in practice who say, 'how would I ever use this in New York?' And that's fine, because we're talking about a different type of context. The context that this would be most readily applied to would be the second or third ring of a second- or third-tier city, where there's fast growth and flexibility. There's also been resistance from different types of Indigenous groups, who have different historical legacies related to colonialism and imperialism – especially in the US and Australia. And so, there have been conversations about how this knowledge should be used, whether it can be used, who it belongs to and whether there are reparations coming from it. And they're all really valid questions, and they spark heated but also incredibly valuable conversations. Some have said that this knowledge isn't to be shared with us: 'why would we share it?' And others want me to highlight these technologies so that they can create some sort of foundation to resist governments coming in and trying to destroy these technologies in the Global South. So, there are very different conversations throughout the Global North and the Global South in relation to how these technologies should be discussed, how they can be used, how they can be talked about and who can talk about them.

JM   There's also a topological logic at work in the book – you group these technologies by types of terrain.

JW   That's right, because you can migrate a technology from
one similar biome to another. So, if you have a wetland technology,
it can apply to another wetland. If you have a forest technology,
it can go to another forest ecosystem. We don't really have those
ecosystems in New York any more – we've erased most of them – so
this is a conversation about not erasing technologies in the Global
South. It's about a different kind of technology that's not high-tech.
It's where humans and ecosystems adapt and evolve to become more
biodiverse. It allows the Global South into the conversation about
technology and climate change. These are technologies that can help
people be less vulnerable in terms of food scarcity, water scarcity
and flooding.

JM   How fundamentally do you think the design industry
needs to reinvent itself?

JW   I think we're already doing it. I think part of the
resistance to change is because the change feels so big. But often it's
not realised that the change is already occurring, and perhaps we're
in the midst of the critical, uphill change that needs to happen. But I
think what we need to acknowledge is that we're *in the change*. And
it's probably always going to be an ongoing process. But I think we
could be more accepting that certain codes need to be innovated.
We have these archaic systems like World Heritage, which upholds
the outstanding value of a pristine ecosystem – but there's nothing
that's pristine any more; we're all touched by climate change. We're
in the midst of a massive adaptation of the way in which humankind
understands and exists on Earth. And I think the place where it's
going to change and where it's already changing is economic
systems. And so, if we're going from globalisation to a different
state of what we call multipolarity, where there's more regionalism
and more localism of trade, economics and politics – as well as
environmental approaches – we can be more responsive to those
needs, which is a good thing. I think we're going see a cascading
effect towards a more literal, or more literate, ecological civilisation.

MAKING THINGS LAST

To end our throwaway society, designers are creating
things we want to invest in, value and maintain.
As most energy is used in making things, it makes
sense to ensure these things have a long life,
that they are designed to be easily repaired with
replaceable parts, and they are designed for
efficient disassembly and recycling after use.
While the efficient use of materials has always
been at the core of good design, many designers did
not consider what happened to their products after
use. The design stage is where action can drive
change. By accepting responsibility for end-of-life,
designers can continue to make an impact on the
environment. But this requires consumers to demand
action and manufacturers to adopt new processes.

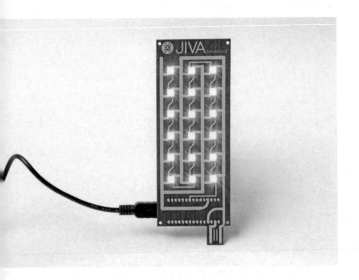

Printed circuit boards (PCBs) contain valuable and
critical metals such as copper, gold and silver fixed
into fibreglass with epoxy resin. A new kind of PCB,
the Soluboard, is designed to dissolve so that these
metals can be recovered. Made of water-soluble,
non-toxic, natural fibres, it could reduce by 60 per
cent the carbon footprint of the 18 billion square
metres of PCB manufactured each year.

Currently, very few people recycle LED (light-emitting diode) lightbulbs, although they contain a variety of critical raw materials. One idea for designing out resource loss is to establish a service to rent new then return spent lightbulbs for recovery. This approach would give companies the financial incentive to design and manufacture bulbs for disassembly.

1   This spread: Service Shirt. Design: Becky Earley, Centre for Circular Design, University of the Arts London

The Service Shirt is a concept for a garment that is designed to last fifty years. It changes and evolves through external remanufacturing processes and sharing cycles with every year to avoid the owner becoming tired of the garment and prematurely disposing of it. The shirt begins in a simple white cut and develops though various patterns and dyeing processes, eventually transforming into a jacket's lining and an accessory. The Service Shirt pushes the idea of use and reuse to the extreme to ensure extended product life.

[OVERLEAF]
Some 90 per cent of old radios, irons and kettles end
up in landfill. This inspired the Agency of Design
to produce three concept toasters that demonstrate
different approaches to end-of-life design. One of
these, the Optimist, is designed to be unbreakable,
with few moving parts. After a costly initial outlay,
it will last for generations. It is made from easy-to-
recycle aluminium.

1 This spread: Fairphone
3, 2019–21. Design:
Fairphone; manufacture:
Fairphone/Arim

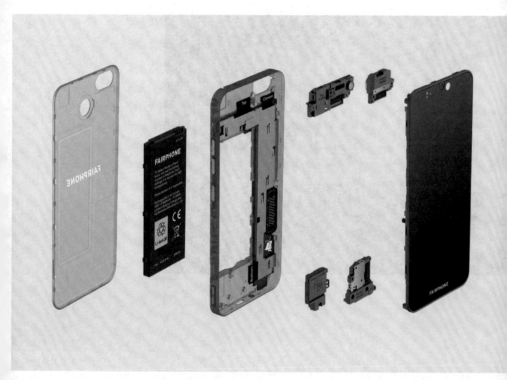

Smartphones make a huge impact on the environment.
The longer we keep our phones, the smaller environmental
footprint they have. Fairphone aims to change our
assumptions about the disposability of mobile devices
by making them easy to dismantle, repair and upgrade.
Each Fairphone is constructed from seven key components,
such as the camera, which can be upgraded rather than
buying a new phone.

In 2003, the Japanese village of Kamikatsu madea
zero-waste declaration. It has since achieved 80
per cent recycling, in contrast to a national rate
of just 20 per cent. Inhabitants separate waste
into more than 45 categories (excluding only items
that are unhygienic, such as nappies, or were
not designed for material separation). They are
encouraged to recycle by a points-based credit
system reflecting the economic impact of waste.

Kamikatsu 45 categories of waste and what they're recycled into:

①	②	③-1	③-2	③-3	③-4	③-5
Re-usables	Organic waste	Aluminum cans	Steel cans	Spray cans	Metal caps	Scrap metals
Kuru-Kuru shop	Compost at home	Aluminum products	Steel products	Metal products	Metal products	Metal products

④-1	④-2	④-3	④-4	④-5	④-6	④-7
Newspaper, Fliers	Cardboards	Magazines, Scrap paper	Milk cartons	Paper cups	Paper carton with aluminum	Hard paper cores
Newspaper	Cardboards	Recycled paper	Recycled paper	Recycled paper	Recycled paper	cardboards

④-8	④-9	⑤-1	⑤-2	⑥-1	⑥-2	⑦-1
Shredded papers	Other papers	Discarded clothes, Blankets	Other clothes	Chopsticks, Woods	Waste oil	Clean plastic packaging
Recycled paper	RPF (Refuse Paper & Plastic Fuel)	Second-hand Clothes, Wipes	RPF (Refuse Paper & Plastic Fuel)	Fire wood, RPF	Composed fodder	Plastic products, RPF

⑦-2	⑦-3	⑦-4	⑦-5	⑧-1	⑧-2	⑧-3
Dirty plastic packaging&products	Styrofoam trays (white only)	PET bottles	PET bottle caps	Clear glass bottles	Brown glass bottles	Other-colored glass bottles
RPF (Refuse Paper & Plastic Fuel)	Styrofoam trays	Clothes	Plastic products, RPF	Clear glass bottles	Brown glass bottles	Glass bottles

⑧-4	⑨-1	⑨-2	⑨-3	⑨-4	⑨-5	⑨-6
Returnable bottles	Other glass, Potteries	Mirrors, Thermometers	Light bulbs, Fluorescent tubes	Dry batteries	Discarded batteries	Lighters
Re-used	Base course material	Mercury & Glass-wool	Mercury & Glass-wool	Metal products	Lead	Metal products

⑩-1	⑩-2	⑩-3	⑩-4	⑪-1	⑪-2	⑫
Large/bulk Metal products	Large/bulk Wooden products	Beddings, Mattresses etc.	Large/bulk PVC, rubber products	PVC, Leather products etc.	Diapers and sanitary napkins	Shells, Hand-warmers etc.
Metals	RPF (Refuse Paper & Plastic Fuel)	RPF (Refuse Paper & Plastic Fuel)	Incineration	Incineration	Incineration	Landfill

⑬-1	⑬-2	⑬-3
Discarded tires	Fire extinguisher	Specific home appliances
RPF (Refuse Paper & Plastic Fuel)	Regenerative fire extinguisher agent & metal products	Recycled by each producers/brands

Zero Waste Center内
Waste Collection Center
OPEN:月～金7：30～14：00　土日7:30～15:30
TEL:050-3438-8110
*Open on Saturdays, Sundays & National Holidays
*Close during Dec.31 to Jan.2

＊Please make sure to wash & dry before bringing in cans, bottles, styrofoam trays, chopsticks, and plastic packaging.
＊Large/bulk waste are accepted during weekdays as well.

1   Framework laptop, 2021.
    Design: Po Yu Chen/Framework;
    manufacture: Framework

The Framework laptop is a lightweight, high-performance
computer with a modular system that is upgradable,
adaptable and repairable. The recommendation is for
most laptops to be replaced every three to five years,
but the Framework is designed to last ten. It can easily
be upgraded with more storage or a new screen, and has a
community marketplace for reselling parts.

1   This spread: Cork House,
    2016. Matthew Barnett
    Howland with Dido Milne
    (CSK Architects) and
    Oliver Wilton (UCL)

The Cork House is constructed from interlocking blocks
of cork and timber, without the need for mortar or
glue. The team behind it has developed a 100 per
cent sustainable product from waste cork, using its
natural properties to create blocks. Designed for easy
disassembly, the bricks can be recovered, reused or
harmlessly returned to the environment at the end of
their lives.

1 This spread: Sling
Lounge Chair, 2021.
Design: Sam Hecht
and Kim Colin/
Industrial Facility,
2021; manufacture:
TAKT, Denmark

The pared-down design of this sustainably sourced and
produced oak-and-linen chair exemplifies the careful use
of resources. Constructed for disassembly, its minimal
components can be easily replaced if worn or broken.
The Sling Lounge Chair's environmental footprint has
been further reduced by designing it to be flat-packed
and easy to transport.

1   adidas Futurecraft Loop
2, a circular design
for a trainer, made
from 100% recycled and
recyclable thermoplastic
polyurethane (TPU).
Design and manufacture:
adidas. Commercial
release 2022.

To develop a circular approach to design and
manufacture, adidas has produced a running shoe from
the recycled material of its first Futurecraft Loop
trainer. Because a single material is used for every
element of the trainer, at the end of life, the TPU
plastic can be ground and melted into new pellets to
form part of the second-generation trainer. This new
system of design requires the user to adapt to the
habit of returning the shoe after use, and by doing
so, keeping the material resource in the supply chain.

GROWING A NO
WASTE FUTURE

Designers are the new alchemists, searching for
ways to transmute existing resources into valuable
new materials. By establishing makeshift labs,
new start-ups or collaborations with scientists,
they experiment and develop bio-materials from
agricultural waste or generate renewable growable
materials rather than extracting ancient ones. Many
projects increase community employment by using
local waste or by-products and promoting innovative
manufacturing techniques.

New materials developed from fungi or algae offer
some of the insulating, lightweight, waterproof
and transparent properties of plastics, but are
non-toxic and designed to degrade. They also create
intriguing 'natural' looks that make us re-examine
our concept of what is 'modern'. This is just the
beginning of a shift towards making materials that
will help to reduce or eradicate the environmental
impact of single-use packaging waste.

1   This spread: Calcareous Arabesque, 2021. Design: Bio-ID Team (Dr Brenda Parker and Prof Marcos Cruz with YaoYao Meng, Dali Alnaeb, Anete Salmane, Dr James Lawrence, Prantar Tamuli); manufacture: BMADE support for fabrication (Prof Peter Scully, Vincent Huyghe, Pradeep Devadass, Mark Burrows); process: Tate & Lyle Sugars (Dr John Kerr, Clara Aymerich)

This 3D-printed wall panel is made from food waste from the sugar-refining process. A 'scaffold for inhabitation', it provides ridges and valleys for plants and wildlife to populate, helping them to thrive within an urban environment. Bio-integrated design fuses biology and architecture, nature and the man-made. Using new technologies and materials, it creates architecture that benefits humans, plants and animals alike.

Waste Lab is developing a range of materials using
the skin of sugar beets. A by-product of the sugar
industry, beet skin is one of the biggest agricultural
waste streams in Poland. Sonia Jaśkiewicz began
working with the cellulose-rich skins for a graduation
project in 2017, and is now developing natural
alternatives to single-use packaging and MDF.

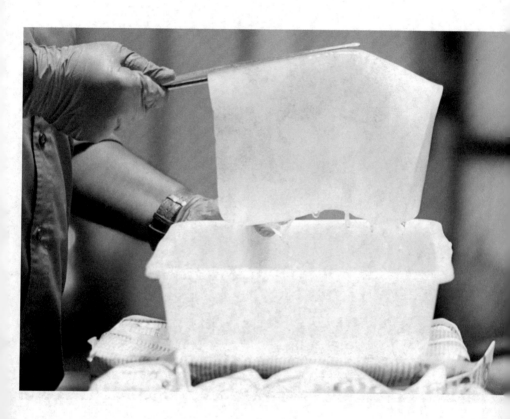

Malai is a new leather-like material made from coconut
water. Coconut-processing factories in India often only
use the flesh of the nut. The discarded water is taken by
the manufacturer, then sterilised and fed with bacteria.
This creates a biofilm that is harvested, mixed with
natural fibres and processed into a sheet material.
Every 4,000 litres of waste coconut water yields 320
square metres of material.

1   This spread: Sea Stone,
2019—ongoing. Newtab-
22, Jihee Moon and Hyein
(Hailey) Choi

Sea Stone is made from the shells of crustaceans
discarded by the South Korean fishing and aquaculture
industries. The dumped shells have disrupted local
ecosystems, but Newtab-22 instead transforms the
calcium carbonate-rich waste into tiles, interior
panels and small objects. Sea Stone is certified
as non-toxic, 100 per cent biodegradable, fireproof
and water resistant. The South Korean government is
funding research to develop, scale and commercialise
the material.

1   Wall paper, raw panel
    and hard panel,
    made from sunflower
    agricultural waste from
    the Camargue, mineral
    and vegetal binders.
    Atelier Luma, 2021.

In the south of France the sunflower is grown for
its oil and only the flower head is harvested. The
stem, regarded as waste, is used by Atelier Luma to
produce alternatives to synthetic insulation and wall
cladding materials for new building projects. The
upscaling from sampling to batch production comes
with several challenges, such as limited material
supply, storage conditions, seasonality and the
non-existent industry for it. All these elements are
deeply studied in the design and development of bio
waste material manufacture.

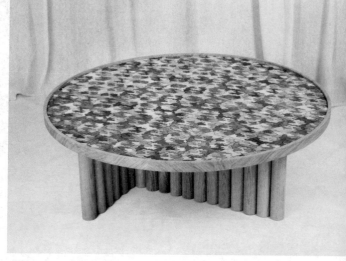

This decorative veneer, used for high-end interiors
and furniture, is made from the husks of endangered
heirloom corn from Mexico. The varieties of native
corn are in decline due to the increased use of
modified imported seed and pesticides. By working
with indigenous communities from Tonahuixtla, its
designer Fernando Laposse provides employment,
supports resilient farming practices and preserves
local biodiversity.

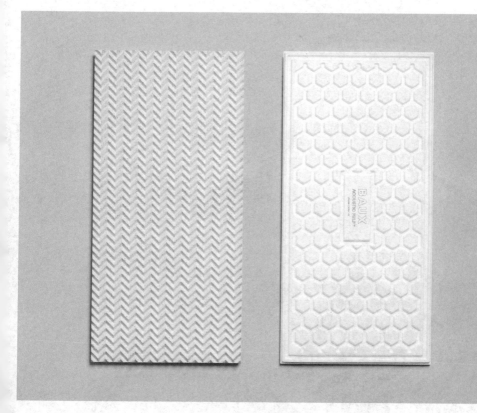

Made with a new 100 per cent bio-based and biodegradable
material, BAUX Acoustic Pulp aims to match the
aesthetics and functionality of petrochemical-derived
alternatives. Based on more than twenty-five years of
research, the panels exploit natural properties found in
plants, such as the strength of potato starch molecules
and the water repellence of lotus flowers, to develop
sustainable solutions to materials and design today.

1   This spread:
    Sony Original paper
    blend packaging

To replace plastic packaging, Sony has produced
a blended material using bamboo and sugarcane
waste. These fast-growing and sustainable crops are
combined with recycled wastepaper. Uncoloured and
embossed rather than printed, the robust material
is used for every part of Sony's noise-cancelling
headphones packaging so that it can be easily
recycled without sorting.

Every passenger on a long-haul flight generates
more than 1kg of waste, most of which is incinerated.
Design studio PriestmanGoode have developed an
alternative onboard meal tray. The design replaces
single-use materials with a combination of the edible,
reusable and biodegradable, including coffee beans
and rice husks.

1   Opposite: Get Onboard
    meal tray, 2019
    PriestmanGoode

2   Below: Zero Takeaway
    packaging scheme.
    PriestmanGoode

Our recycling systems and materials need rethinking to
avoid single-use waste. This research project redesigns
delivery packaging for takeaway meals. Inspired by
Japanese bento boxes and Indian tiffin tins that
hold multiple dishes in a stacked container, this new
packaging uses sustainable materials that can be washed
and reused, and is transferable between restaurants.
Customers are reimbursed when the packing is returned,
with additional incentives (such as discounts on future
orders) being offered to embed good habits.

1   This spread: Nuatan
     vessel crafting plastics!
     studio, Vlasta Kubušová
     and Miroslav Král

These 3D printed vessels are made from Nuatan, a
plant-based material developed by crafting plastics!
studio that behaves and looks like plastic. It can be
used for injection moulding, 3D printing, extruding,
computer-programmed milling, laser cutting, heat
pressing, vacuum forming and other standard industrial
processes. Nuatan has a lifecycle of between one
and fifty years, but, when put into an industrial
composter, degrades into water, carbon dioxide and
biomass within 120 days.

1   This spread: Mycelium
    insulation, 2016.
    Designer: Ehab Sayed;
    manufacture: BIOHM

BIOHM has created a mycelium insulation panel for the
construction industry. Mycelium, a filament produced
by fungi, is a natural alternative to petrochemical-
based construction materials used in thermal and
acoustic insulation and as a fire retardant. More
than 300 strains of mycelium are fed on waste from
other industries, including plastic, coffee grounds,
agricultural waste, wood and citrus peel, using
local rubbish and creating new jobs.

1 This spread: Biofabric
tennis dress, 2019.
adidas × Stella McCartney

Durable plastics like polyester and nylon are used
to make 90 per cent of sportswear, but designers
and scientists are developing new fully biodegradable
fabrics with high-level stretch and fit properties.
This tennis dress is made from bioengineered protein
thread. Genetically modified yeast is fermented with
sugar and water to produce silk proteins, which are
extracted and spuninto fibres.

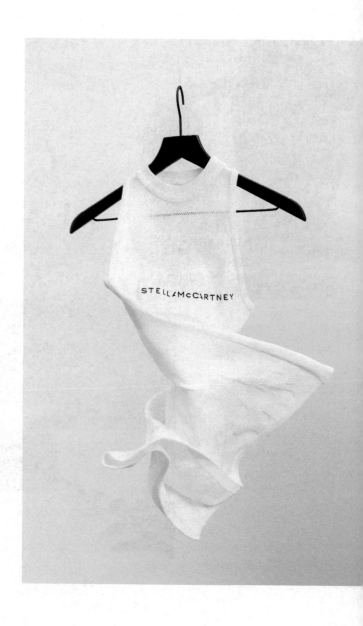

1 This spread: Ello Jello.
Designer: David Christian;
manufacture: Evo & Co.

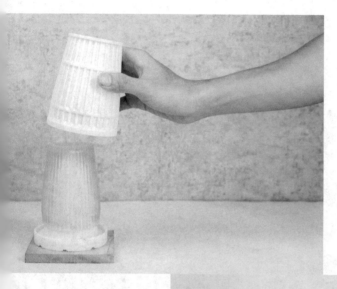

Ello Jello is an edible cup for events and parties,
made from seaweed and other plant-based materials.
As well as providing secure work for local seaweed
farmers, Evo & Co. wants to make its products
commercially competitive, which is crucial for
the widespread uptake of bio-products. Currently,
one metre of seaweed-based material costs about
US$20, while plastic can cost as little as 50¢.

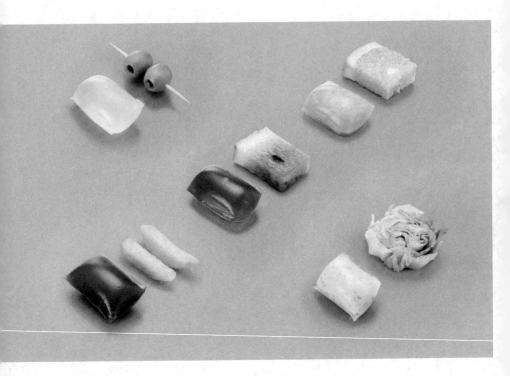

Notpla (short for 'not plastic') is a biodegradable
seaweed-based material that aims to replace single-
use plastic packaging. Notpla products include
Ooho, an edible bubble for liquids and condiments,
and a coating for takeaway boxes. Some species of
seaweed can grow two metres in 24 hours, making
them sustainable and abundant. To date, Notpla has
replaced more than 300,000 single-use plastic items.

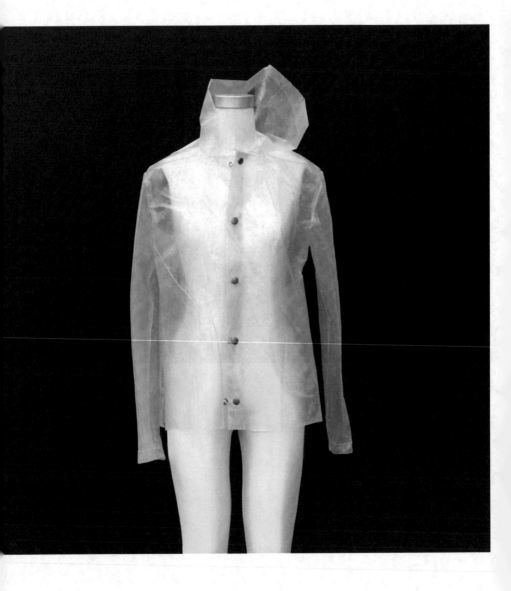

This carbon-negative raincoat is made from a petroleum-
free, algae-based plastic. The designer, Charlotte
McCurdy, believes that consumption can be guilt-free
and environmentally friendly if we use materials that
hold or sequester carbon rather than releasing it. The
raincoat highlights that a carbon-negative future is
achievable: we can imagine it, we can wear it, we can
take the steps to instigate it.

1 Opposite: After
   Ancient Sunlight, 2019.
   Charlotte McCurdy

2 Below: Sequin dress,
   2020. Design: Charlotte
   McCurdy and Phillip Lim

Collaborating on a couture dress, Phillip Lim and
Charlotte McCurdy demonstrated that bio-materials can
replace toxic products without compromising aesthetics,
feel or function. This gown is made from a carbon-
neutral fabric with algae-based sequins applied to it.
Sequins are usually made from oil-derived plastics. In
2019, 33 million new sequined garments were sold in the
UK and 7 million went to landfill, contributing to the
mounting microplastics problem.

1   This spread: Lovely
    Trash Column, 2021. BLAST
    (Biological Laboratory
    of Architecture and
    Sensitive Technologies)

This column, made from discarded takeaway coffee
cups, turns waste into a building material. The cups
are digested by mycelium, the root network of fungi,
and converted into a biological paste that can be 3D
printed. Transforming waste into construction materials
helps to deal with the 30,000 tonnes of coffee cups
discarded in the UK each year that cannot be recycled
due to their plastic lining.

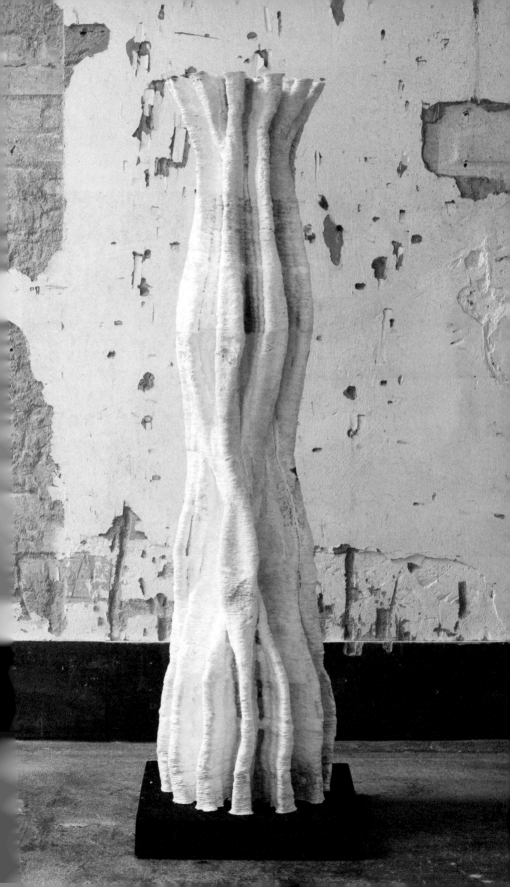

1   This spread: TECLA
(a 3D printed house),
2021. Design: MC
A – Mario Cucinella
Architects; manufacture:
WASP Italy

Built in Ravenna, Italy, this house 3D printed out of
clay demonstrates a circular model of construction.
WASP's crane 3D printer takes this technology to a
new scale. Combining reusable or recyclable materials
from the site – in this case clay – with innovative
technology, this method of construction is adaptable
to any location and updates the ancient art of building
earth structures.

1   This spread: Algae
     Platform, 2017–21.
     Design: Atelier Luma/
     Luma Arles, I.C.W Studio
     Klarenbeek & Dros;
     manufacture: Vegeplast

The design and research lab Atelier Luma, based in
Arles in the south of France, is a multi-disciplinary
team that develops local solutions for ecological,
economic and social change. Its pioneering research
into algae explores its use and production and how
algae can be integrated into the urban environment.
Using 3D printing and injection moulding, Atelier
Luma designs various applications that reflect the
diversity and qualities of locally grown algae.

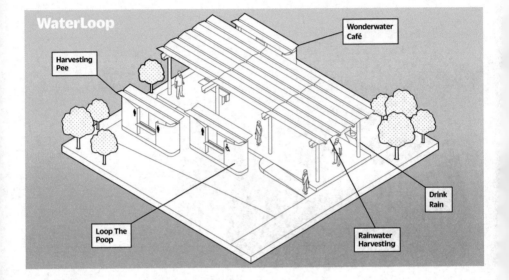

1 This spread: Water Loop. Design: Anupama Kundoo Architects; concept: Jane Withers Studio; design: Anupama Kundoo Architects; water adviser: Dr Naho Mirumachi, King's Water Hub at King's College London; sanitation adviser: Dr Tse-Hui Teh, UCL. Commissioned by and created in collaboration with British Council

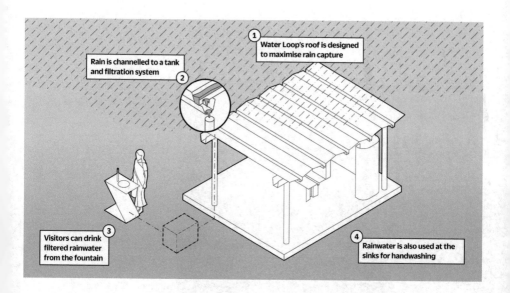

1 Water Loop's roof is designed to maximise rain capture

2 Rain is channelled to a tank and filtration system

3 Visitors can drink filtered rainwater from the fountain

4 Rainwater is also used at the sinks for handwashing

This low-cost modular structure provides free public toilets that are maintained by the profits from a local café and adaptable for different sites. The model uses a closed loop of rainwater collection and exploits the nutrients from human waste to grow food. It provides a sustainable design solution to sanitation and scarcity of water.

1 This spread: Project
Coelicolor, 2019–
ongoing. Natsai Audrey
Chieza, Faber Futures,
in collaboration with
Professor John Ward

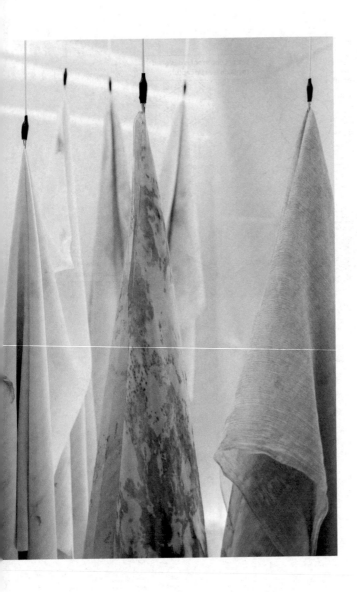

The soil-growing bacteria *Streptomyces coelicolor*
can act as a fabric dye. The bacterium's pigment
creates a colour-fast finish without the use of
chemicals, significantly reducing water consumption
during industrial dyeing. This example of cross-
disciplinary research between designers and biologists
shows the potential for the organic world to provide
solutions to our wasteful ways of living.

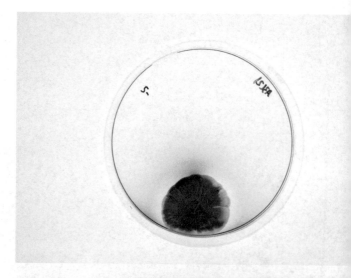

Designers are looking at ways to counter the impact
of the environmental crisis. EcoLogicStudio have
developed BioBombola, a zero-waste food source, created
by cultivating an algae garden at home. Algae absorbs
carbon dioxide and oxygenates the environment more
effectively than house plants, while also providing a
nutrient-rich vegetable protein that can be harvested
and consumed.

1   This spread: Digital
sampling for the Peak
Performance FW21
collection. Design:
The Fabricant; 3D
rendering: Daniele
Scarante, Bram Siebers
– The Fabricant

Every shop garment has been through a huge process
of sampling to determine fabric, pattern, sizing and
palette. Peak Performance worked with digital-only
fashion house The Fabricant for FW21, using hyper-
realistic 3D drawings and digital sampling processes
to replace the exchange of physical samples. Adjustments
were made at the click of a button. This dramatically
reduced their carbon footprint, saving energy, water,
time and money, and eliminating physical waste.

ANCIENT WISDOM

The concept of progress as forward-looking
innovation informed by new technology is a
seductive path which has shaped the twentieth
and twenty-first centuries, but ancient ways and
systems also have much to teach us. The Western
approach of mastering and exploiting nature could
be replaced by holistic and sustainable structures
and systems that have little or no environmental
impact, opting for minimal material use, cost and
maintenance.

As city dwellers living away from nature, we
need more reminders that not all cultures and
societies live in opposition to nature. Many
continue to respect and live sustainably with
their surrounding ecosystems.

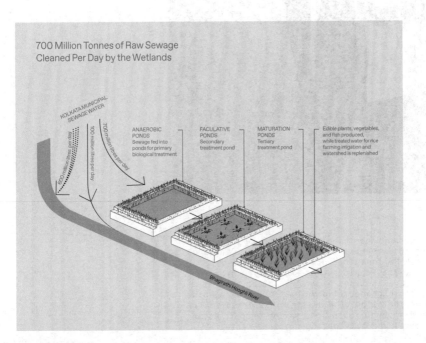

700 Million Tonnes of Raw Sewage
Cleaned Per Day by the Wetlands

KOLKATA MUNICIPAL
SEWAGE WATER

100 million litres per day
700 million litres per day

ANAEROBIC
PONDS
Sewage fed into
ponds for primary
biological treatment

FACULATIVE
PONDS
Secondary
treatment pond

MATURATION
PONDS
Tertiary
treatment pond

Edible plants, vegetables,
and fish produced,
while treated water for rice
farming irrigation and
watershed is replenished

Bhagirathi Hooghli River

1   This spread: Bheri
    wastewater aquaculture
    and a diagram of
    the different water
    treatment stages.

Illustration opposite:
from *Lo-TEK, Design
by Radical Indigenism*
by Julia Watson.
Illustrations by Julia
Watson, illustration
treatment by Berke
Yazicioglu

In the early twentieth century, fishermen outside
Kolkata developed a fishery that doubled as a waste
treatment system. By filtering the sewage from this city
of 15 million people through a staged series of ponds,
they found that the water was gradually cleaned and the
fish yields rose. In the century since, this piece of
the East Kolkata Wetlands has become a vital resource
for the city, providing fertilisation, food and a
sewage treatment plant, all in one natural ecosystem
– something that would require millions of dollars'
worth of industrial plant.

1 This spread: Dalston
Works, Hackney, London,
2017. Waugh Thistleton
Architects.

COMMISSION: WAUGH THISTLETON

Dalston Works was the world's largest cross-laminated
timber (CLT) building on completion. The landmark
project was proof that CLT could be used as a sustainable
alternative to steel in large-scale construction and
high-density housing. The ten-storey building weighs
only one-fifth of an equivalent building of this size and
needed 80 per cent fewer deliveries during construction.

COMMISSION: WAUGH THISTLETON

255   1   This spread: Multiply
and the cross-laminated
timber it was built from   POST WASTE

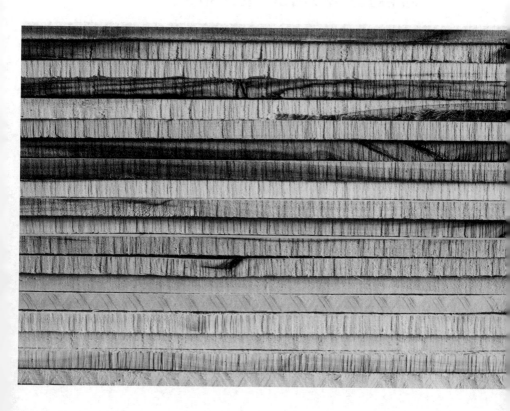

Waugh Thistleton worked with the American Hardwood
Export Council on a modular structure called
Multiply, made from cross-laminated timber. The aim
was to demonstrate the structural potential of woods
that are under-used in North American forests — in
this case tulipwood — which need active managing
for their own health. The modules were assembled in
different configurations multiple times, and for the
Design Museum were repurposed into a new screening
room, extending the material's life even further.

COMMISSION: LIFE FROM LIGHT.
SONY DESIGN CENTRE EUROPE AND
MERGRIM/TAKAHISA MITSUMORI

1   This spread: Stills
from *Life from Light*,
interactive installation
by Sony Design Centre
Europe and Mergrim/
Takahisa Mitsumori

The Sony Design Centre Europe created an interactive
installation aimed at connecting visitors with the
hidden life of a forest. By focusing on the fungi,
mycorrhizal structures and other micro-organisms on
the forest floor, we get a visceral experience of a
rich world where things grow and rot, and where the
circle of life revolves. As the visitor moves across
the screen, this organic life lights up in sync with
her movements, accompanied by a responsive soundtrack
by sound artist Mergrim/Takahisa Mitsumori.

THE SYSTEMIC DESIGN FRAMEWORK

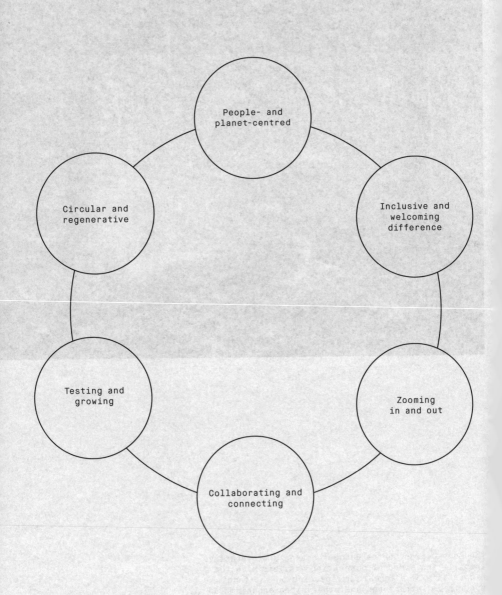

PEOPLE- AND PLANET-CENTRED

Focusing on the shared benefits of all living things

INCLUSIVE AND WELCOMING DIFFERENCE

Creating safe, shared spaces and language to bring
in multiple and marginalised perspectives

ZOOMING IN AND OUT

From the micro to macro, from root cause to hopeful
vision, from the present to the future, from the
personal to the wider system

COLLABORATING AND CONNECTING

Seeing a project as one element in a wider movement
for change

TESTING AND GROWING

Making things to see how they work and help more
things emerge

CIRCULAR AND REGENERATIVE

Focus on existing assets – physical and social
– and how we can reuse, nurture and grow these

NOTES

INTRODUCTION

1   Greenpeace released an animated advertisement in 2021 about how many plastic bottles are disposed of in this country, criticising the UK Government's inaction, in which it coined the useful hashtag #Wasteminster.

2   https://www.theguardian.com/environment/2021/jul/01/call-for-global-treaty-to-end-production-of-virgin-plastic-by-2040 [Accessed 1 July 2021]; also: more data at www.plasticseurope.org [Accessed 1 September 2021].

3   David Farrier, *Footprints: In Search of Future Fossils* (London: Fourth Estate, 2020), 103.

4   https://www.ciel.org/project-update/plastic-climate-the-hidden-costs-of-a-plastic-planet/ [Accessed 1 September 2021].

5   The term was proposed by Formafantasma as part of their Ore Streams project.

6   www.theguardian.com/environment/2021/may/17/uk-plastics-sent-for-recycling-in-turkey-dumped-and-burned-greenpeace-finds [Accessed 1 September 2021].

7   Many of these ideas and the products thereof are nascent or niche, and the first thing that critics will say is 'How do you scale that up?' Well, maybe 'scaling up' is part of the problem, and in the end bigness is best replaced by small-scale and localised.

8   Anna Lowenhaupt Tsing, *The Mushroom at the End of the World* (Princeton, NJ: Princeton University Press, 2015), 3.

E-WASTE AS A CHALLENGE FOR DESIGN AND SOCIETY

1   United States Environmental Protection Agency, *Toxicological Review of Trichloroethylene* (Washington, DC: EPA, September 2011), cfpub.epa.gov/ncea/iris/iris_documents/documents/toxreviews/0199tr/0199tr.pdf [Accessed 29 July 2021].

2   Mr Advocate General Jacobs, Opinion of Mr Advocate General Jacobs delivered on 24 October 1996. Criminal proceedings against Euro Tombesi and Adino Tombesi (C-304/94), Roberto Santella (C-330/94), Giovanni Muzi and others (C-342/94) and Anselmo Savini (C-224/95), No. Joined cases C-304/94, C-330/94, C-342/94 C-224/95 (European Court 1997).

3   John Gallinatti et al., 'Managing a Large Dilute Plume Impacted by Matrix Diffusion:

MEW Case Study' (June 2012), 21, 27, frtr.gov/
pdf/meetings/jun12/presentations/gallinatti-
presentation.pdf [Accessed 29 July 2021].

4   Apple Computer Inc., 'iPhone 12 Product
Sheet', 2020, 2, www.apple.com/environment/pdf/
products/iphone/iPhone_12_PER_Oct2020.pdf [Accessed
29 July 2021].

5   Max Liboiron, *Pollution Is Colonialism*
(Durham, NC: Duke University Press, 2021).

6   Kris De Decker, 'How Circular Is the
Circular Economy?', *Uneven Earth*, November 2018,
unevenearth.org/2018/11/how-circular-is-the-
circular-economy [Accessed 29 July 2021].

7   Weston Baxter, Marco Aurisicchio and
Peter Childs, 'Contaminated Interaction: Another
Barrier to Circular Material Flows: Contaminated
Circularity', *Journal of Industrial Ecology* (May
2017), doi:10.1111/jiec.12612; NU Blum, M Haupt
and CR Bening, 'Why "Circular" Doesn't Always
Mean "Sustainable"', *Resources, Conservation
and Recycling*, 162 (November 2020), 105042,
doi:10.1016/j.resconrec.2020.105042; Thomas
Schaubroeck, 'Circular Economy Practices May
Not Always Lead to Lower Criticality or More
Sustainability; Analysis and Guidance Is Needed
per Case', *Resources, Conservation and Recycling*,
162 (November 2020), 104977, doi:10.1016/j.
resconrec.2020.104977; Markus A Reuter, Antoinette
van Schaik and Miquel Ballester, 'Limits of the
Circular Economy: Fairphone Modular Design Pushing
the Limits', *World of Metallurgy*, no. 2 (2018), 13.

8   Josh Lepawsky, 'Towards a World of Fixers:
Examining Barriers and Enablers of Widely Deployed
Third-Party Repair for Computing within Limits',
in *Proceedings of the 7th International Conference
on ICT for Sustainability*, ICT4S2020 (New York, NY:
Association for Computing Machinery, 2020), 314–20,
doi:10.1145/3401335.3401816 [Accessed
29 July 2021].

9   Kevin Purdy, 'Is This the End of
the Repairable iPhone?', IFixit (blog), October
2020, www.ifixit.com/News/45921/is-this-the-end-
of-the-repairable-iphone [Accessed 29
July 2021].

10   Mary H O'Brien, 'Being a Scientist
Means Taking Sides', *BioScience*, vol. 43,
no. 10 (1993), 706–8, doi:10.2307/1312342.

BEYOND THE ECONOMY OF WASTE

1   For fuller details, see Robin Murray,
Zero Waste (London: Greenpeace Environmental
Trust, 2002).

2   www.fao.org/food-loss-and-food-waste/
flw-data [Accessed 10 August 2021].

3   Kate Soper, *Post-Growth Living: for an
alternative hedonism* (London: Verso, 2020), 124.

4   https://www.itv.com/news/2021-06-21/
amazon-destroying-millions-of-items-of-unsold-
stock-in-one-of-its-uk-warehouses-every-year-itv-
news-investigation-finds.

5   Jonathan Chapman, 'From fashion to
field: shredded cotton clothing used to help
grow future crops', *Guardian* (17 June 2021).

6   A recent media study found that four out
of five articles on the economy presumed growth
to be positive without offering any reasons why.
See J. Lewis, *Beyond Consumer Capitalism: Media
and the Limits to Imagination* (Cambridge: Polity
Press, 2013), 124–78; cf. Jason Hickel, *Less is
More: how degrowth will save the world* (London:
Penguin, 2020), esp. 101–25.

7   Kate Raworth, *Doughnut Economics:
Seven Ways to Think Like a 21st-Century Economist*
(London: Random House, 2017).

8   See Kate Soper, 'Alternative Hedonism,
Cultural Theory and the Role of Aesthetic
Revisioning', *Cultural Studies*, vol. 22, no. 5
(September 2008), 567–87, and Soper, *Post-Growth.
Living*, 157–9.

REPAIR CULTURE

1   Rosalind Williams in *The Durability
Factor: A Guide to Finding Long-Lasting Cars, Housing,
Clothing, Appliances, Tools, and Toys*, ed. Roger B.
Yepsen, Jr (Emmaus, PA: Rodale Press, 1982), 12.

2   Kyle Wiens, 'The New MacBook Pro:
Unfixable, Unhackable, Untenable', *Wired*, 14 June
2012: https://www.wired.com/2012/06/opinion-apple-
retina-displa [Accessed 23 September 2021].

3   Jason Koebler, 'Tim Cook to Investors:
People Bought Fewer New iPhones Because They
Repaired Their Old Ones', *Vice*, 2 January 2019:
https://www.vice.com/en/article/zmd9a5/tim-cook-
to-investors-people-bought-fewer-new-iphones-
because-they-repaired-their-old-ones [Accessed 23
September 2021].

4   This and the following quotation
are from the Ellen MacArthur Foundation
webpage, 'What is circular economy': https://
www.ellenmacarthurfoundation.org/circular-
economy/concept [Accessed 23 September 2021].

AWAY FROM A NEW ARCHITECTURE

1   St Jerome, *Commentary on Ezekiel*,
Preface to Book I.

2   Janet DeLaine, 'The Economics of
Construction in Imperial Roman Architecture',
keynote paper at SAHGB Annual Symposium,
June 2021.

3   UN Environment Programme, '2020 Global
Status Report for Buildings and Construction',
globalabc.org/sites/default/files/inline-
files/2020BuildingsGSR_FULLREPORT.pdf (p. 48).

4   Barnabas Calder, *Architecture: From
Prehistory to Climate Emergency* (London: Pelican,
2021), esp. Part 2, pp. 197–444.

5   Architects Climate Action Network is
campaigning for the introduction of embodied-
carbon monitoring and restrictions.

6   The Association of Plastics
Manufacturers: www.plasticseurope.org/en/about-
plastics/building-construction [Accessed 10
August 2021].

7   www.architectsjournal.co.uk/news/
retrofirst [Accessed 10 August 2021].

8   www.architectsjournal.co.uk/news/
jenrick-says-permitted-development-provides-big-
opportunity-to-bulldoze-buildings [Accessed 10
August 2021].

9   Arctic Council Sustainable Development
Working Group, *Zero Arctic: Concepts for carbon-
neutral Arctic construction based on tradition*,
2020 report, downloadable from oaarchive.arctic-
council.org/handle/11374/2541 (p. 89).

10   Janet DeLaine, *The Baths of Caracalla:
A Study in the Design, Construction, and
Economics of Large-scale Building Projects in
Imperial Rome* (Cambridge: Journal of Roman
Archaeology, 1997).

INDEX

PICTURE CREDITS

CONTRIBUTORS

Barnabas Calder, senior lecturer in architecture,
University of Liverpool

Natsai Audrey Chieza, founder and CEO,
Faber Futures

Josh Lepawsky, professor in the Department of
Geography, Memorial University of Newfoundland

Justin McGuirk, chief curator, the Design Museum

Liz Ricketts, co-founder and director,
OR Foundation

Kate Soper, emeritus professor of philosophy,
London Metropolitan University

Lee Vinsel, associate professor of science,
technology and society at Virginia Tech

Julia Watson, architect and author of *Lo-TEK:
Design by Radical Indigenism*

ACKNOWLEDGEMENTS

This book was published in conjunction with
the exhibition *Waste Age: What Can Design Do?*
at the Design Museum, London, 23 October 2021
to 20 February 2022.

Curators
Gemma Curtin, Justin McGuirk

Assistant Curator
Lara Chapman

Curatorial Research Assistants
Maddalena Castellani, Hannah Skevington

Exhibitions Project Manager
Gabria Lupone

Exhibitions Project Coordinator
Georgia Mulvaney-Thomerson

Exhibition Designers
Material Cultures, SPIN

The Design Museum would like to thank the
advisory committee that helped steer the
curatorial conversations and content. They
are: Natsai Audrey Chieza, Marcos Cruz, Rebecca
Earley, Joe Iles, Zoe Laughlin, Joycelyn Longdon,
Sophie Thomas and Jane Withers. We would also
like to thank three people who fed into the
curatorial concept at an early stage: Jane
Withers, Mariana Pestana and Duncan Baker Brown
all contributed valuable ideas that found their
way into the exhibition and book.

Associate Sponsor

Supported by Cockayne Grants
for the Arts, a donor advised
fund at London Community Foundation

COCKAYNE **The London Community Foundation**

Design Museum Publishing
Design Museum Enterprises Ltd
224–238 Kensington High Street
London W8 6AG
United Kingdom

designmuseum.org

First published in 2021
© 2021 Design Museum Publishing

978-1-872005-54-6

Publishing Manager
Mark Cortes Favis

Project Editor
Robert Davies

Assistant Editors
Giulia Morale, Alex Todd

Picture Researchers
James McLean, Anabel Navarro

Copyeditor
Ian McDonald

Proofreader
Simon Coppock

Design
SPIN

Artworker
Chris Benfield

Many colleagues at the Design Museum
have supported this book, and thanks
go to them all.

Distribution
UK, Europe and select territories
around the world

Thames & Hudson
181A High Holborn
London, WC1V 7QX
United Kingdom
thamesandhudson.com

USA and Canada
ARTBOOK | D.A.P.
75 Broad Street, Suite 630
New York, NY 10004
United States of America
www.artbook.com

Printed and bound in the
United Kingdom by Pureprint

The publisher has made efforts to reduce
wastage and the environmental impact of
producing this book. It was printed by
the world's first CarbonNeutral© printer,
using vegetable-based inks, recycled
stock for the cover and sustainable
paper sources for the text. Printing
in the UK means that we were able to
minimise transport and we have avoided
shrinkwrapping, lamination and other
plastic-heavy production processes.